Francis Frith's
Lighthouses

Photographic Memories

Francis Frith's
Lighthouses

David Wilkinson & Martin Boyle

FRITH
BOOK Co

First published in the United Kingdom in 2001 by
Frith Book Company Ltd

Hardback Edition 2001
ISBN 1-85937-257-0

British Library Cataloguing in Publication Data

Francis Frith's Lighthouses
David Wilkinson & Martin Boyle

Frith Book Company Ltd
Frith's Barn, Teffont,
Salisbury, Wiltshire SP3 5QP
Tel: +44 (0) 1722 716 376
Email: info@francisfrith.co.uk
www.francisfrith.co.uk

Printed and bound in Great Britain

Front Cover: St Anthony's Lighthouse and the Manacles Reef 1890 24222

Contents

S
Ha
Ind
Fre

Francis Frith: *Victorian Pioneer*

FRANCIS FRITH, Victorian founder of the world-famous photographic archive, was a complex and multi-talented man. A devout Quaker and a highly successful Victorian businessman, he was both philosophic by nature and pioneering in outlook.

By 1855 Francis Frith had already established a wholesale grocery business in Liverpool, and sold it for the astonishing sum of £200,000, which is the equivalent today of over £15,000,000. Now a multi-millionaire, he was able to indulge his passion for travel. As a child he had pored over travel books written by early explorers, and his fancy and imagination had been stirred by family holidays to the sublime mountain regions of Wales and Scotland. 'What a land of spirit-stirring and enriching scenes and places!' he had written. He was to return to these scenes of grandeur in later years to 'recapture the thousands of vivid and tender memories', but with a different purpose. Now in his thirties, and captivated by the new science of photography, Frith set out on a series of pioneering journeys to the Nile regions that occupied him from 1856 until 1860.

Intrigue and Adventure

He took with him on his travels a specially-designed wicker carriage that acted as both dark-room and sleeping chamber. These far-flung journeys were packed with intrigue and adventure. In his life story, written when he was sixty-three, Frith tells of being held captive by bandits, and of fighting 'an awful midnight battle to the very point of surrender with a deadly pack of hungry, wild dogs'. Sporting flowing Arab costume, Frith arrived at Akaba by camel seventy years before Lawrence, where he encountered 'desert princes and rival sheikhs, blazing with jewel-hilted swords'.

During these extraordinary adventures he was assiduously exploring the desert regions bordering the Nile and patiently recording the antiquities and peoples with his camera. He was the first photographer to venture beyond the sixth cataract. Africa was still the mysterious 'Dark Continent', and Stanley and Livingstone's historic meeting was a decade into the future. The conditions for picture taking confound belief. He laboured for hours in his wicker dark-room in the sweltering heat of the desert, while the volatile chemicals fizzed dangerously in their trays. Often he was forced to work in remote tombs and caves where conditions were cooler. Back in London he exhibited his photographs and was 'rapturously cheered' by members of the Royal Society. His reputation as a photographer was made overnight. An eminent modern historian has likened their impact on the population of the time to that on our own generation of the first photographs taken on the surface of the moon.

Venture of a Life-Time

Characteristically, Frith quickly spotted the opportunity to create a new business as a specialist publisher of photographs. He lived in an era of immense and sometimes violent change. For the poor in the early part of Victoria's reign work was a drudge and the hours long, and people had precious little free time to enjoy themselves. Most had no transport other than a cart or gig at their disposal, and had not travelled far beyond the boundaries of their own town or village. However,

by the 1870s, the railways had threaded their way across the country, and Bank Holidays and half-day Saturdays had been made obligatory by Act of Parliament. All of a sudden the ordinary working man and his family were able to enjoy days out and see a little more of the world.

With characteristic business acumen, Francis Frith foresaw that these new tourists would enjoy having souvenirs to commemorate their days out. In 1860 he married Mary Ann Rosling and set out with the intention of photographing every city, town and village in Britain. For the next thirty years he travelled the country by train and by pony and trap, producing fine photographs of seaside resorts and beauty spots that were keenly bought by millions of Victorians. These prints were painstakingly pasted into family albums and pored over during the dark nights of winter, rekindling precious memories of summer excursions.

The Rise of Frith & Co

Frith's studio was soon supplying retail shops all over the country. To meet the demand he gathered about him a small team of photographers, and published the work of independent artist-photographers of the calibre of Roger Fenton and Francis Bedford. In order to gain some understanding of the scale of Frith's business one only has to look at the catalogue issued by Frith & Co in 1886: it runs to some 670 pages, listing not only many thousands of views of the British Isles but also many photographs of most European countries, and China, Japan, the USA and Canada -- note the sample page shown above from the handwritten *Frith & Co* ledgers detailing pictures taken. By 1890 Frith had created the greatest specialist photographic publishing company in the world,

1835, with its beam set at 72ft above sea level. The recorded visible distance for the light was put at 16 nautical miles.

Yet even with the bright light of St Anthony's providing a positive marker for shipping, Commander Lory still continued his relentless campaign of condemning its location. He sent a long letter to the Board of Trade in 1855, in which he reported the loss of the 500 ton barque 'John'. This wooden sailing ship left Plymouth on the night of 2 May 1855. On board were 18 crew and 268 passengers, who were looking forward to a new life in America. While the captain was drinking heavily below decks, a south-westerly gale blew up. At the helm was a very inexperienced crewman, who was caught completely off guard by the ferocious wind. At 1.00am on 3 May the keepers at St Anthony's logged the 'John' as it made its approach into Falmouth harbour. But within minutes, they saw that the 3-masted barque had changed course in an attempt to go back into the English Channel. In less than an

hour, the 'John' had run head on into the Manacles reef. Distress flares were sent up by the keepers, which brought out the Porthoustock lifeboat.

After battling through horrendous conditions, the lifeboat reached the 'John'; 80 terrified survivors were found clinging to the rigging of her broken masts. Then without warning the drunken captain and 10 of his intoxicated crew forced their way past the frightened passengers towards the lifeboat. In total disbelief, the lifeboat coxswain watched as screaming passengers were wrenched from the rigging to fall to their deaths in the treacherous sea. It then became necessary for the lifeboat crew to defend themselves and to subdue the drunken men with ropes. Yet even though this action forced the coxswain to return to port where the crew were arrested, he and his faithful crewmen managed to make numerous trips back to rescue the survivors. By 8.00am the lifeboat had saved the lives of 91 people - sad to say, 196 people were lost. Over the following 2 weeks, wreckage and bodies washed up along the coast.

St Anthony's Lighthouse c1960 S33138

Tragedy struck another fateful blow to Falmouth Bay during the latter part of 1898. On this occasion people would die simply because someone forgot to make a course change. On 13 October 1898 the 'Mohegan' left Gravesend on the start of her second transatlantic crossing to New York. On board was her master, Captain Griffiths, and a compliment of 106 passengers and crew. The weather was fine with a comfortable south-easterly breeze. Originally, this 8500-ton liner was named the 'Cleopatra'; she was built by the Earle Shipping & Engineering Company in Hull. Due to a dock yard strike, the ship was a year late in being completed. Her original owners, the Wilson Shipping Line, feared that this extended delay would bring about a financial disaster, and so the 482ft-long ship was sold before she was launched.

But following the launch her boilers had caused a great deal of problems, especially during her maiden voyage. This effectively delayed her arrival in New York by four days. Also, Captain Griffiths felt that his ship had a bad feel about it; he based this upon a superstition that it was a bad omen to have the original ship's bell for the 'Cleopatra' still on board. As the 'Mohegan' entered the English Channel, her course was set, but no-one noticed a mistake in the heading. Even when the watch changed, this error went unnoticed. At around 6.00pm on 13 October, coxswain James Hill, at the Porthoustock lifeboat lookout, spotted the liner approaching the treacherous Manacles. He thought this was only a temporary problem, and that the ship would soon alter course. When this failed to happen, he let off two 'blue fires', but they went unnoticed.

Twenty minutes later, Captain Griffiths went to the bridge following complaints from the passengers about the increasingly rough passage. As he entered the bridge, the loud clanging of the Manacles bell was heard; if they were this close, he knew there was no way to avoid the reef. The 'Mohegan' hit the Vase Rock at full speed, which embedded her rudder into the hard granite. She then skimmed across the main group of rocks known as the Voices, which ripped a gigantic hole in her hull. Just minutes later the once proud 'Mohegan' sank stern first. Only 14 people survived this tragedy. A mass grave can be seen in St Keverne churchyard, where a simple granite headstone lists the names of those who perished.

Very little changed in the operational status of the St Anthony's lighthouse until 1954, when the station was electrified. On 22 September a floating crane arrived to take down the massive 2-ton bell. Trinity House were asked by the local people if it would be prepared to donate the bell to Penwerris Church. This was agreed to, as long as an special sermon was given once a year for those upon the sea. After its removal, the bell stood on sleepers at the eastern breakwater at Falmouth. Later it was taken on a trailer towed by a large steam engine and placed on the lawn in front of the church. Yet for nearly 5 years the bell was not moved, and it began slowly to sink into the ground. Two problems had arisen. Firstly, the belfry was too small, and not strong enough to support the weight of the bell; secondly, nobody knew how to get the bell up to the top of the tower without demolishing most of the front portion of the church. Money was also a serious problem. In the summer of 1959 the bell was collected by the Taylor Foundry and taken to Loughborough, where it was melted down.

In 1987, after 152 years of faithful service, the St Anthony's lighthouse was automated. Generations of keepers ended their tradition and left the station. Although an attendant keeper regularly visits the lighthouse, St Anthony's is now controlled and monitored by the Trinity House Depot in Harwich, Essex. However, it is still an important navigational aid, and is part of the chain of lights around Cornwall; they include Lizard Point, Longships and Wolf Rock.

Polperro Lighthouse

The 13th-century fishing village of Polperro originally belonged to the ancient Raphael Manor, which is mentioned in the Domesday Book. Fishing has been the principal occupation of its inhabitants for centuries, and pilchards were often caught in abundance to be sold far and wide. Its harbour is owned by the local parish ratepayers and is administered by a Board of Harbour Trustees, established by Act of Parliament in 1894 'for the improvement, maintenance and regulation of the harbour'. All of the 15 Trustees are unpaid volunteers, and serve on the committee for 3 years. Income for the Trust comes from harbour dues and receipts from the Heritage Museum. These funds are then re-invested into the Polperro Harbour in new development, along with the maintenance of the quays and piers.

The roots of Polperro lie back in an era when it was the community's belief that there was such a thing as 'legalised smuggling'. This became a way of life following the arrival of a very charismatic benefactor. Zephaniah Job's arrival in the small Cornish fishing village of Polperro in the early 1770s radically changed the life of the community. Within a short period, he carefully ensured that his life was well catered for by managing the business side of Polperro's smuggling trade. He hired lawyers in Cornwall and in London to represent any of the smugglers who went to court. If a smuggler was sent to prison, Mr Job supported the family of the smuggler. His ability to manage money and to keep well-documented records proved beneficial for several Polperro ships that were fitted out as privateers between 1777 and 1815. One of the more bizarre projects for Zephaniah Job was the issuing of his own Polperro banknotes. These were printed for him by his London agent, Alderman Christopher Smith, who also handled the transfer of money to the Guernsey merchants for the tea, gin, brandy and tobacco supplied to the Polperro smugglers.

In 1798 a Polperro smuggling boat called the 'Lottery' was involved in an incident in which a customs officer was killed. One of the crew, Tom Potter, was later tried for murder at the Old Bailey and executed. This effectively halted the Polperro smuggling business. Zephaniah Job died at Crumplehorn at the age of 75, having never married and without making a will. However £1,442 in cash was found in his house, which was more than enough to honour all of his personal bank notes.

The lighthouse shown in the picture was established in 1904 and is set on to the cliff to the east of the harbour. It is 16ft in height with a light set at 141ft above sea level, with the base enclosed by a rubble stone boundary wall. When in service this light was visible for 12 nautical miles. In 1958 it was discontinued, and 3 new lights were established.

Polperro, The Lighthouse 1928 81341

Newlyn

Newlyn, The Lighthouse & Breakwater 1920 69751B

The fishing port of Newlyn is located just a mile to the west of Penzance. It is home to the largest fleet of fishing boats in the south of England, which has a significant effect on the economy of the entire area. Pilchards were once the major product of the local industry - they were processed and packed, and then sent all around the world.

Newlyn is considered to be a far better refuge for ships running for a safe haven during bad weather than Penzance harbour. During the late 19th century, it was decided by the Harbour Board to establish a permanent light to guide vessels into port. As Newlyn was a busy fishing town, it became necessary to provide a suitable navigational reference at night. During its busiest years as a fishing port, Newlyn became especially crowded between June, July and August when boat-loads of pilchards were being landed. Vessels from Looe, Mevagissey and St Ives would fill the harbour and leave little room for the local boats. Restrictions were introduced to parts of Newlyn during the early 1950s, when the south pier was only to be used by stone ships and other larger commercial vessels.

There were 2 lights established in Newlyn Harbour, one on each of its breakwater piers. The south pier light, the one we see in the above picture, provided a white flash every 5 seconds. On the north pier the light was a fixed red beam, but it also showed a white illumination over the harbour. A local harbour attendant lit each light at sunset and extinguished them around sunrise. Later, the small lighthouse was modernised and fitted out with acetylene equipment and lights. It was in around 1960 that these lights were electrified and completely automated. A visitor to Newlyn in 1960 would have found 3 small hotels and many shops, but early closing on Wednesdays. Buses ferried the local people to Penzance at very frequent intervals. There are numerous small streets and alleys behind the main road (it runs around the harbour and connects Newlyn with Penzance and Mousehole). Many of these streets have unusual names, such as the Fradgan, Gwavas Quay and Bowjey Hill. Amongst these narrow streets are fishermen's cottages and pubs which are very much the home territory of the locals, but visitors are always made welcome.

Off the promenade leading from Penzance into the port is the Newlyn Orion Gallery. This gallery exhibits the work of a wide variety of artistic talent, with particular emphasis on the past and present work of local artists in both contemporary and traditional fields. While small, it has a remarkable reputation and is well known around the world.

Although the Newlyn light is not considered to be a lighthouse in the true sense, it is no less important, especially for local shipping. To understand this comment, it is correct to state that lighthouses are really specified as being lights that have been established solely for shipping in general. In most cases, the smaller lights came under the responsibility of the Harbour Authorities, and not Trinity House.

Newlyn harbour is also the home base of the Penlee lifeboat, the 'Mabel Alice', which replaced the previous 'Solomon Browne', which was so sadly lost at sea with all hands. On 19 December 1981 the crew of the Penlee lifeboat, the 'Solomon Browne', were called to give assistance to the 1,400-ton coaster 'Union Star'. This Dublin-registered merchant vessel was on her maiden voyage from Ijmuiden to Arklow. The weather conditions were some of the worst ever seen, with south-easterly winds reaching hurricane force 12 and waves peaking at 60ft. Just 8 miles east from the Wolf Rock lighthouse, the captain of the 'Union Star' reported an engine failure. He gave the location of the vessel, which was drifting dangerously close to the cliffs between the Tater-du and Boscowan Point.

The first rescue attempt was made by a Royal Navy Sea King helicopter, piloted by Lt-Cdr Russell L Smith, USN. But conditions were so bad that he was unable to lift anyone off the ship without endangering the lives of his men or the aircraft. Mountainous seas swept the 'Union Star' towards the cliffs as the crew of the 'Solomon Browne' made repeated attempts to position their lifeboat alongside. On two occasions, horrendous waves lifted the lifeboat onto the deck of the 'Union Star'. Luckily, it slid back into the sea stern first. From the helicopter, the pilot and aircrew watched as the 'Solomon Browne' was picked up by a huge wave and slammed against the side of the 'Union Star'. On this occasion, the lifeboat recovered, and was seen to be still under the control of her coxswain, William Trevelyan Richards. A message was received from the lifeboat that 4 of the crew had been rescued. But it then appeared that even under these horrific conditions the 'Solomon Browne' was about to make another approach to rescue the remaining men on the 'Union Star'. As the helicopter was about to leave

the scene, radio contact was lost with the lifeboat. Just 10 minutes later, her lights disappeared. The pilot brought his aircraft around on a full circle at the same time as horrendous waves battered the 'Union Star' and capsized her close to the Tater-du Lighthouse.

The news of the tragedy was relayed to the lifeboat 'Vincent Nesfield', which was temporarily on station at Sennen Cove. She was launched, but this put her on a heading into the full force of the storm. While this vessel continued its attempt to reach the wreck scene, the Isles of Scilly and the Lizard-Cadgwith lifeboats, helicopters, HM Coastguard coastal rescue teams, and several fishing vessels joined in the search for the missing mariners. This search continued relentlessly throughout the night. By the following day, it was apparent that 8 lifeboat men and the 8 crew from the Union Star were lost. Some of the bodies have never been recovered.

Newlyn, The Pier Lighthouse 1920 69749

The Lizard

Lizard Point, The Lighthouse 1895 36225

The massive headland of Lizard Point is on the heel of south Cornwall. Its notoriety derives from it being one of the most treacherous mariners' nightmares around the coast of England. During the winter the sea literally smashes into this jagged shoreline, sending its spray cascading over the summit of the 170ft-high Lizard Point like heavy rain.

To voyagers from the west, bound for the English Channel, the Lizard is the first point of English land to be seen. It is therefore not surprising that Lizard Point became the first site for a planned maritime light, especially with its reputation as 'the ships' graveyard'. This photograph shows the lighthouse when both towers were operational.

The history of the Lizard light begins during the 16th century, with its owner Sir John Killigrew. This

knight of the realm obtained a Royal Letter Patent from Elizabeth I in 1570 for the erection of a navigation light on his land at Lizard Point. Considering that he headed a family that was engaged in privateering, smuggling, piracy and the plundering of wrecked ships, his motive for such a venture seems questionable. His brazen attitude regarding these activities saw him not only funding the escapades of the west country pirates, but often accommodating them at his mansion home, Arwenack House.

In 1557 Sir John Killigrew and his pirates seized a Spanish galleon as she rounded Land's End. Her cargo of silver bullion was valued at £10,000. Under the guise of 'legalised privateering', Sir John paid his 20% duty to the Royal Treasury and retained the remaining fortune. Sir John was then considered philanthropic by the local people: most of the bullion was used to finance the building of new houses and roads around Falmouth harbour. At the Royal court, Sir John was not looked upon as a pirate, but a loyal subject of Queen Mary I. His activities clearly provided the Privy Purse with a steady income. Many west country noblemen eagerly financed his ventures, which often trebled their original investment. When his vessels returned from their plundering sorties, Sir John openly sold the proceeds and organised the movement of any smuggled goods around every part of Cornwall. Even the 'revenue men', or customs officers, accepted the money from Sir John as part of their terms of employment.

Sir John Killigrew's cleverest move was to influence Elizabeth I into making him the Commissioner for Piracy in Cornwall in 1559. His mandate required him to seek out those 'undesirables' and bring them to justice. In this exalted position no one questioned why he regularly mixed with known pirates in the taverns.

It would therefore seem that Sir John Killigrew was liked by everyone in the Royal court, but in fact this was not the case. The Lord Lieutenant for the West Country and his associate, the Clerk of the Privy Council, were strongly opposed to the activities of this knight of the realm. From numerous discussions with French and Spanish ambassadors, it was clear that the actions of Sir John were affecting the relationship between the three countries. Yet it appeared that this Royal favourite had the full blessing of the Queen, which made it virtually impossible for anyone to discredit him. Sir John covered his tracks meticulously; he ensured that his activities were well organised, with suitable bribes paid or violence carried out by his henchmen.

Yet one person that Sir John had no control over was his wife. Lady Killigrew supported her husband's activities, and even went on some of the raids with his pirates. But greed became her downfall following the arrival of the 144-ton Spanish merchant ship 'Marie' during January 1583. With a lull in the war between England and Spain, the 'Marie' sought refuge in Falmouth harbour after a severe storm. While repairs were being carried out, her owners accepted the hospitality of the Sir John at Arwenack House. On 8 January, Lady Killigrew and several pirates from Penryn, along with members of her household, seized the 'Marie' and sailed her out of Falmouth. Even the duty officer at Pendennis Castle was bribed to ensure that the ship could leave port unharmed. When the ship was 10 miles out to sea, her skeleton crew was thrown overboard by the pirates. A course was then set for Roaring Bay in Ireland, where within two days of arriving the 'Marie' and her cargo were sold. Once the proceeds were divided, Lady Killigrew and the pirates split up and made their separate ways back to Cornwall.

The owners of the 'Marie' complained to Sir John Killigrew, but although numerous people were questioned by the militia, nothing was found. However, the Spaniards were not satisfied at the way the investigation was handled; they reported the matter to the Earl of Bedford and Edmund Tremayne. This news was welcomed by these two men. They took the opportunity to intervene, especially as it finally gave them a chance to discredit the Killigrew family. Under intense interrogation a Falmouth tavern owner,

Lizard Point, The Lighthouse 1904 52237

Elizabeth Moore, admitted lying to the original investigators, and that two men, Henry Kendal and John Hawkins, were not at her inn when the 'Marie' went missing. When the men were questioned in Pendennis Castle, they confessed to being among the pirates. But in an attempt to gain their freedom, they implicated Lady Killigrew as the leader. At last Edmund Tremayne, Sir Richard Grenville and the Earl of Bedford had enough evidence to destroy Sir John's credibility at court.

Using his power as Lord Lieutenant of Cornwall,

Kendal were rejected. On 25 May 1583 they were executed. Their bodies were left hanging outside the Launceston court house for three days, with the intention of deterring acts of piracy.

In 1584 Sir John tried to sell his Patent for the Lizard light, but no one took up the option. With no light being established, he surrendered his rights to the Privy Council. Two months later Sir John died, a virtual bankrupt and heavily in debt to the sum of £10,000, the amount it cost him to secure his wife's release.

Lizard Point, The Lighthouse and the Rocks c1960 L62173

Edmund Tremayne ordered the arrest of the accomplices and openly prosecuted them at the Launceston assizes. In April 1583, Hawkins, Kendal and Lady Killigrew were found guilty and sentenced to death for piracy. Sir John Killigrew was devastated at the outcome of the court case, and openly stated that his wife had been falsely accused in a conspiracy instigated by his enemies. His cousin, William Killigrew, a groom in the Queen's household, obtained a pardon for Lady Killigrew just hours before she was due to be executed, but mercy pleas for Hawkins and

By the latter part of the 17th century, there was a dramatic increase in sea trade passing Lizard Point, which also brought about a rise in ships being wrecked to near epidemic proportions. Plundering and wreck-scavenging became commonplace for heartless communities, who often killed any survivors so that they could not make any claim for salvage.

In the 18th century, Lizard Point was bought by Thomas Fonnereau, a wealthy merchant from the Channel Islands. With the help of Captain Richard Farish, a proposal was made to Trinity House for the erection of four lighthouses on the headland. Over the next 12 months, consideration was given to the proposals by Captain Farish, but by November 1749 he had been taken seriously ill. To ensure that the petition and application remained active, Captain Farish changed his will to formally make Thomas Fonnereau an equal partner in the intended venture. In January 1750, two months before Trinity House formally consented to the petition, Captain Farish died. Negotiations were then finalised with Thomas Fonnereau over the lease licence of the Lizard Point lights.

When levies were imposed, the amount due was for each light that a ship passed; but when the Letter Patent was drafted, it clearly stated that the Lizard Point was classed as only one light, irrespective of how many towers were constructed. The lease was issued to Thomas Fonnereau for a period of 61 years at an annual rent of £80. As the lessee, he was authorised to collect by 'compulsory means' the sum of 'one half-penny sterling per laden ton' from all English ships (excluding His Majesty's ships of war), and double for foreign vessels. This levy had to be paid for any ship which passed the light in either direction along the English Channel within a 20-mile radius.

Trinity House appointed two Elder Brothers, Captain Joseph Cartert and Captain Edward Smith, to oversee the construction of the Lizard Point lighthouses. It was their duty to ensure that the towers were positioned to provide the optimum visual aid for the mariner, both as day beacons and for the lights at night. An architect from Penzance was commissioned to draw up all the plans, based upon the designs specified by the two Elder Brothers. By the time the drawings were prepared, the towers had been designated to be 216ft apart. Each of the towers was to be built in an octagonal design, with its walls constructed from rubble granite masonry quarried from the headland. Thomas Fonnereau and his

Cornish builders began the construction of the Lizard Point lighthouses on 24 May 1750.

Access inside each tower was by means of a geometrical stone stairway, which wound its way to the 'bellow blowers' below the gallery. At this level a wooden pole ladder allowed the attendants to climb up to the lantern room.

Photograph 36224 shows the original steam-powered Brown Brothers siren (far left).

The actual lantern was constructed from cast iron framing with flat panes of glass. Its roof originally

Lizard Point, The Lighthouse 1895 36224a

consisted of iron rafters covered with copper panels. On top of this conical roof was erected a large cylindrical chimney with a strange-looking ball finial cowl. Inside of each of the lanterns were large iron braziers. From below these units were iron pipes, which fed air into the bottom portion of the coal fires. At the other end of this network of pipes were large leather bellows. To ensure that the attendants never slacked in their duties, or went to sleep on the job, a watchman was employed. If the light did not maintain its expected illumination, he would sound off a blow horn, or fire a blast through his blunderbuss, which was primed with gunpowder and dried corn. Coal for the fires was either carried up the staircase, or hauled through the centre of the towers to the top of the lighthouse. On the floor below the bellow blowers area, just enough coal was stored for each nights requirements, with the remainder in an enclosure close to each tower. All the cinders and ash were dumped inside a rubble stone-walled trough, close to the watchman's cottage.

On the night of 15 July 1751, the two lights were officially lit for the first time, 127 years after Sir John Killigrew abandoned the original Lizard Point light. It was not until September 1752 that Thomas Fonnereau received his official lease documents for the Lizard lights. This document verified that the station had been built according to the specifications laid down by Trinity House. When reading through his lease papers, Thomas Fonnereau was shocked to note that two extra clauses had been added to the documents. One item which incensed him was the last clause, which read: 'and after the expiry of the said period of 61 years, the lessee shall give up the lighthouses, buildings, roads etc, and one and a quarter acres of land known as Lizard Point, and to leave peaceably without a penny claim of compensation from the Corporation of Trinity House'. This photograph below shows the majestic Douglass fog horns (far left).

For 19 years Thomas Fonnereau battled with Trinity House in an attempt to have the expiry clause

Lizard Point, The Lighthouse 1904 52232

deleted from his lease. His lawyers argued that the Corporation did not have the exclusive right to take over the land and property owned by their client. For six years, lawyers for both parties continued to drag the dispute through numerous courts of appeal;

finally, in 1771 a panel of 3 judges and a jury decided that the clause was legal. Legal fees for his unsuccessful court actions, plus the fact that the fees charged for the lights barely covered the cost of maintaining the lights, forced Thomas Fonnereau to declare himself bankrupt in 1780. At this time, no one else was interested in taking over the lease for Lizard Point, so Trinity House brought in its own keepers.

Coal remained the only fuel source for the Lizard Point lights, until Trinity House obtained an Act of Parliament in 1811 to use oil. New 13ft-high lanterns just over 10ft in diameter were also erected on top of the towers. Inside each lantern stood an iron column on to which was fixed 19 Argand lamps with catoptric reflectors. When these lights were brought into service on Thursday 16 January 1812, they had a recorded visible distance on a clear night of 21 nautical miles.

Once the new lights were operational, Trinity House demolished the night watchman's cottage and constructed a 216ft-long building between the two towers. Accommodation was also required for the expected eight keepers and their families, who would be living on station. When the first of these keepers were posted to Lizard Point, there was a total of 36 people living there, including children.

To many people it will seem strange that a lifeboat service was not established near Lizard Point until 1859. This was a tragic situation when we consider the disastrous record of ships being wrecked along these shores, which made the area the worst around the whole of England.

Near the end of November 1874 James Nicholas Douglass supervised the start of the modernisation programme for the Lizard lights. His designs for the Lizard station included a large engine room, a coal and coke store, a full-size workshop and a purpose-built engineers' apartment. There were also quarters built for the expected four keepers, who would be required to maintain the new equipment and machinery. To ensure that suitable accommodation was provided, the existing roof on the central dwellings was to be removed and a second storey constructed on top.

Inside the spacious machine room, three 10hp (horse power) calorific engines were installed. The units installed at Lizard Point at this time were engines manufactured by A & F Brown of New York. These units drove four large generators by means of webbed belts gripping huge cast iron wheels fixed to a long steel shaft. The third engine was for the sole use of driving the air compressor that powered the fog siren. While the changes to electricity were in progress, first order dioptric lens assemblies were installed into each of the lantern rooms. Both of these units was capable of magnifying the light source to a phenomenal 8 million candle power (candelas). The recorded visible distance for these lights was reputed to be about 22 nautical miles. They were first lit on 29 March 1878.

Lizard Point, The Lighthouse c1960 L62163

James Nicholas Douglass also supervised the installation of his air-powered siren. When compressed air was forced through the siren, a powerful sound was produced; it was transmitted out of upright cast iron hook-shaped trumpets with huge bell mouths.

During the summer months of 1895, the first two diesel oil engines were installed. Only one of the former calorific engines was retained, and today it has been preserved as a tourist attraction. By 1903 the Corporation had decided to discontinue the west light and to install a new optical apparatus and clockwork drive mechanism into the eastern tower. On 1 November 1903, the new revolving optic and light was brought into service. It was recorded to have a light that was visible for nearly 30 nautical miles.

Communication for the keepers at this time was either by flags or by flashing hand-held lamps. The telegraph system did not come to Lizard Point until 1920, when Marconi completed his experiments in the purpose-built shack on Bass Point. This building is still there, and is being preserved by the Trevithick Trust. On 5 February 1940 Lizard Point had its first telephone installed. Its number was Lizard 231. Even today, this is still the last three digits for calling the station.

Seventy-two years after electricity first came to the Lizard Point lighthouse, Trinity House finally managed to have the station connected to the national power supply. Two of the existing generators and diesel engines were upgraded to act as standby units in case of mains failure. On 15 April 1998, Trinity House engineers arrived at Lizard Point to install the new satellite navigation system (DGPS) along with its tall mast. Within 6 months the station was automated. Then, on 16 July 1998, the keepers completed their last tour of duty after 247 years of manned lighthouse keeping at Lizard Point.

Today, all aspects of the operational side of Lizard Point are monitored from the Trinity House control centre in Harwich. However, there is a very charismatic former Principal Keeper still at the Lizard, who is the attendant for this lighthouse. He started his career in the Lighthouse Service at Lizard Point, and was also its last Principal Keeper.

The Wolf Rock Lighthouse

Barely visible from Land's End in Cornwall, the isolated granite Wolf Rock lighthouse stands facing the full fury of the Atlantic. In terms of bitter winters and atrocious sea conditions, there is only one other lighthouse that is more exposed to the elements, and that is the Bishop Rock.

Before a tower was erected on this dangerous reef, numerous beacons were built, but within a short time the sea had washed them away. On one occasion, a bronze wolf was cast with a hole through its centre. The intention was to fix this object on to the rock so that the wind blew through the bronze figure to make the sound of a wolf. However, the Trinity House records state that after 4 days of trying to reach the Wolf Rock, the project was abandoned.

An insight into the dangers posed by the Wolf Rock and its reef is clearly shown by the events involving the Prussian barque 'Astrea' on 16 March 1861. During heavy seas, this vessel was dangerously close to the Wolf Rock before her captain could take any avoiding action. After running at full sail onto the steepest part of the rock, huge waves crashed over her and swept two longboats full of crewmen away to their deaths. The sea then smashed the remaining lifeboats in their davits. As the captain tried to assist an injured man, a water cask fell on him. With the barque settling deeper into the water, the 10 remaining crewmen carried their seriously-injured captain to the top of one of the masts.

For 2 hours the 'Astrea' remained afloat, and at last the Newlyn lugger 'Triumph' arrived on the scene. But there was no way to reach the stricken men without risking the loss of the lugger. To make matters worse, no one could understand what the crew of the Prussian ship were saying. Also the lugger had only one small dinghy, which would have sunk as soon as

The Wolf Rock Lighthouse, the Lantern and Gallery c1891 S73305

it reached the water. Just as the captain of the lugger was about to get closer to the 'Astrea', a huge wave washed her off the rock. Within minutes, she sank stern first. From her complement of 28 crew, the injured captain and his young Prussian cabin boy survived.

Following this tragic event, Trinity House was given permission to erect a lighthouse on the Wolf Rock. It was designed by James Walker in 1861, and in March 1862 the contract began. Lookouts were posted on the highest point of the rock to warn the workers about any waves that were about to overshoot the site. When this occurred, the men grabbed hold of their safety ropes until the sea subsided. Although many were battered and bruised, no one was lost; but after one year into the contract, its designer James Walker died.

William Douglass then took over from his brother James to complete the building of the Wolf Rock tower. On 1 January 1870, the Wolf Rock light was lit for the first time. It stands 115ft from its foundation rock to its gallery, with its beam set at 110ft above the highest spring tide level. Its beam was visible to shipping for about 16 nautical miles.

**The Wolf Rock Lighthouse
The Lantern and Gallery
c1891** S73305A

During both World Wars, the Wolf Rock lighthouse became an observation post for the Admiralty. In 1942 several attacks were made by German aircraft, but luckily their bombs bounced off the rock and exploded in the sea. When these sorties failed the pilots used the tower for gunnery practice, but even then very little harm was done.

In November 1947, three keepers were marooned in the Wolf Rock lighthouse owing to hurricane force storms. By February 1948 the situation was becoming extremely serious, so Trinity House sent a Westland Sikorsky helicopter from the Culdrose Naval Air Base to make an attempt to lower supplies to the keepers. Even with the spray reaching nearly to the lantern, the flight was successful. Another 10 days would pass before a relief ship could take the keepers off the rock.

In 1955 the Wolf Rock lighthouse became the first rock-based tower to have electric generators installed. In the event of possible electrical failure, the former oil lamps could be re-introduced.

At about 5.00am on 3 November 1962, Cornish coastguards saw the lights of a large trawler 2 miles off shore. On her present heading, it appeared that the ship would clear Land's End, and then change course towards Dieppe. Yet for some inexplicable reason this did not happen; the vessel was now in direct line with the Wolf Rock. Coastguards and the keepers at the Wolf Rock lighthouse fired off warning flares. The trawler then made a sudden change of course, but this time she was sailing directly towards the Cornish coast. Further flares were sent up, but these went unanswered. Within half an hour, flares were sighted above the cliffs near the Land's End Hotel. Rescue services raced to the scene to find the 250-ton trawler 'Jeanne Gougy' on the rocks near Gamper Bay. Coastguards sent up parachute flares, which revealed a group of men huddled together near the bridge of the trawler.

Rocket-powered safety lines were fired onto the stricken vessel, but as one of the crew tried to catch it a huge wave swept him overboard. Suddenly a mountainous wave threw the trawler on to her side. At about 9.30am, the Sennen lifeboat picked up the body of the seaman who had been washed overboard. About half an hour later, a helicopter from RAF Chivenor located another body. By this time, the coastguards and the rescue services believed that it was doubtful if anyone had survived. Just after 10.00am, the helicopter pilot began his flight back to base. Within 10 minutes, a woman in the crowd shouted that she had seen a hand waving from the wheelhouse. As the rescue services were recalled to the scene, a huge wave smashed away part of the wheelhouse to reveal 4 men, who scrambled on to the shattered decking.

As the helicopter was about to land at RAF Chivenor, the pilot was ordered to return. On its arrival it hovered over the wrecked 'Jeanne Gougy' while lines were thrown to the stranded men by the coastguards. Within 20 minutes the battered men were hoisted to safety, but there was still an injured man inside the shattered wheelhouse. In atrocious conditions, Flight Sergeant Eric Smith talked the pilot of the helicopter into allowing him to be lowered to rescue the stricken seaman. After a great deal of tricky manoeuvring, Flight Sergeant Smith was able to put a sling around the seaman and hoist him to the safety of the cliffs above.

Although Flight Sergeant Smith was told that it was extremely unlikely that anyone else could have survived, he insisted on being lowered back on to the trawler for a closer look. As he swung to the rear of the battered bridge, he was surprised to find a small terrified boy. Even though he was thrown against the bridge by the strong winds, he managed to rescue the boy. Not satisfied with leaving the incident at that stage, he insisted on going back once more to see if anyone else was alive. Only after the pilot ordered him to return to the helicopter did Flight Sergeant Smith relent. Flight Sergeant Smith was later awarded the George Medal for his actions in rescuing the survivors from the 'Jeanne Gougy'. The death toll for the 'Jeanne Gougy' was 11 men, including the captain. The reason why this tragedy occurred has never been discovered; the reason died with the skipper.

A mystery still surrounds the tragic loss of a keeper on 18 December 1969. He was last seen fishing from the winch room, with the safety barrier correctly positioned. Although a full search of the area was made by a lifeboat, his body was never found.

On 3 November 1973, the Wolf Rock lighthouse became the first rock-based tower to have a helicopter pad erected above its lantern. This not only allowed a safe and regular means for relieving the keepers, but also brought about the deliveries of equipment for automating the station. On 3 June 1987 the Wolf Rock was automated, and the keepers left the station for the final time. For the keepers, this would be the end of something that was not just a job, but a way of life. Without a doubt, it took a very special breed of person to endure the tremendous pounding from the Atlantic while stationed in the Wolf Rock lighthouse. Even after over 130 years of treacherous weather conditions and mountainous seas, the Wolf Rock still shows a light for mariners of all nations so that they can avoid the dangerous rocks that she marks.

Below we see the keepers being relieved.

The Wolf Rock Lighthouse
The Landing and the Old Beacon c1891 S73305B

St Agnes

Established in 1680, the St Agnes lighthouse in the Isles of Scilly was designed and built by two Trinity House Brothers, Captain Simon Bayly and Captain Hugh Till. The tower stands 74ft high; it originally had a coal-burning fire for its light, which was set at 138ft above sea level. It is recorded that on a clear night this fire could be seen for nearly 16 nautical miles.

During the construction of the St Agnes lighthouse, the local residents did all they could to disrupt the builders. Most of these people strongly believed that a light would effectively take away their livelihood, which derived from the rich winter harvest of ships wrecked around the islands. Under the guise of 'custom and descent', these impoverished people relied on the cargoes salvaged from the lost vessels. In order to stave off gangs of wreckers who were intent on stopping the erection of the St Agnes lighthouse, Trinity House enlisted the help of the militia in Penzance.

St Agnes, The Lighthouse c1876 8469

St Agnes was often shrouded in mist or fog, and from a westerly direction the light could not be seen during heavy rain. This problem was considered to be the cause of greatest shipping disaster around the Isles of Scilly. On 21 October 1707, Admiral Sir Cloudisley Shovell grew increasingly concerned that the true position of his fleet was unknown. He called together the commanders and masters of the fleet to attend a meeting on board his flagship 'Association'. This armada of ships included the 'Lennox', the 'Le Valeur', the 'Phoenix', the 'Eagle', the 'Romney' and the fire ship 'Firebrand'. Their assumed position had been set as somewhere close to the French coast, but the master of the 'Lenox' believed they were close to the Isles of Scilly. After a vote, the admiral ordered the 'Lenox', the 'Le Valeur' and the 'Phoenix' to proceed to Falmouth; the rest of the fleet were to follow them a short time later.

Within an hour, disaster struck. The 'Association', the 'Eagle', the 'Romney' and the 'Firebrand' mistook the St Agnes light for one along the French coast. After altering their course, they sailed on to rocks near St Mary's Island. Nearly 2,000 men perished with the total wreck of all the ships. When Sir Cloudisley Shovell's body was found by one of the wrecking community, the fingers were cut off to get his heavy gold rings.

In 1911, Trinity House decided that the St Agnes lighthouse was no longer suitable; a new light was established at Peninnis Head on St Mary's Island. Since that time, the St Agnes lighthouse has been in private hands and used for holiday accommodation. Today it is looked upon more as a private museum, and much of the original coal and oil lighting equipment is preserved. The former granite base for the original coal-burner is still in the yard at St Agnes.

Bishop Rock Lighthouse

Trinity House chose the Bishop Rock for the site of a lighthouse because it is the most westerly point of the Isles of Scilly. This rock is also the most prominent outcrop of the Western Reef, which covers an area of nearly 10 square miles. The Bishop Rock is believed to have been named during the 16th century - its distinctive shape is that of a bishop's mitre. The dark pink colour of its granite adds the final touch. Some sources say that this outcrop is part of the Bishops and Clerks; in fact, the Bishops and Clerks are islands and dangerous rocks near the South Bishop lighthouse off the coast of Pembrokeshire.

Among the numerous ships which have been wrecked around the Isles of Scilly was the 'Royal Oak', in the first recorded incident that referred to the Bishop Rock, on 18 January 1666. A report following this disaster was sent by one of her junior officers, Mr Daniels, to the shipowners. In it he stated that there was no cause for the tragedy. Captain Robb Locke, the master of the 'Royal Oak', ordered his men to go topside to see if there was a clear passage through the reef. With darkness surrounding the vessel, it was impossible to fix a safe course, so Captain Locke ordered the main front anchor to be dropped. But as soon as the

Bishop Rock, The Lighthouse 1890 24895A

anchor took hold, a huge wave spun the 'Royal Oak' and smashed her against the rocks. In order to reduce the top weight of his stricken ship, Captain Locke ordered his crew to chop down the masts. But this action was too late. A further onslaught of waves pounded the helpless vessel into the rocks.

Within a few minutes the 'Royal Oak' was a total wreck. From a compliment of 32 crew, only 8 survived. Mr Daniels was one of these men; along with the other survivors, he scrambled to the nearest low rock for safety, but within minutes the relentless waves had washed them back into the sea. Frantically they swam towards sections of wreckage, which miraculously carried them to the relative safety of the Bishop Rock. Most of these men were badly injured or bleeding, and for comfort they huddled together on the slippery rock.

On 4 September 1839, the 'Theodorick' became the first reported vessel to actually hit the Bishop Rock. The weather conditions were severe, with a heavy mist. This merchant ship's cargo was classified as 'general'. Within minutes of hitting the Bishop Rock, she sank with the loss of everyone on board. Close to this wreck lies another vessel, the 'William Preston', which sank on its maiden voyage from Odessa, after hitting the Bishop Rock in February 1842. Once more the deadly sea claimed the lives of everyone on board.

There have been three towers erected on this isolated rock off the shores of the Isles of Scilly. The first of these was established between 1848 and 1850. However, on the night of 5 February 1850 while the workforce was ashore, a tremendous storm ravaged the Islands and destroyed the cast iron piled tower. Within 12 months the second structure was being built, but this time out of solid granite masonry. After 7 years of at times life-threatening work, the Bishop Rock light was first lit on 1 September 1858. This light was recorded at being shown from 110ft above sea level.

In May 1875 the keepers witnessed one of the most tragic ship disasters that have occurred around the Isles of Scilly when the Glasgow-built 'Schiller' was wrecked on rocks close to the lighthouse. During the night of 7 May, her master, Captain Thomas, was very concerned about being in a dense blanket of fog. He posted lookouts around the ship, and offered a magnum of champagne to anyone who spotted the Bishop Rock light. Believing his ship was too far to the east of the Islands, Captain Thomas altered course to a more westerly direction. Less than an hour later, the ship ran on to the Retarrier Rocks close to the lighthouse.

When the distress rockets were sent up, these were mistaken for the customary flares normally shown when a liner was about to enter port. As panic set in, the Captain was forced to fire his revolver into the air; he threatened to shoot the first man who tried to get into any of the lifeboats before the women and children. Near the midship saloon, 50 women and children huddled together, but a gigantic wave crashed down and washed them into the sea. From the original complement of passengers and crew, only 42 survived out of a total of 355 people on board.

Bishop Rock, The Lighthouse 1890 24895B
Detail of the lighthouse's double lantern and massive bi-form optic.

The present lighthouse was built between 1883 and 1887, mainly because the previous structure was becoming unsafe owing to the battering from the Atlantic seas. It was first lit on 25 October 1887, with its light set at a majestic 144ft above sea level. During the years that this lighthouse was manned, the keepers were often stranded for weeks at a time because no relief could be made. On 12 December 1992 the Bishop Rock lighthouse was automated, and the keepers left the station for the last time.

The Longships Lighthouse

At the beginning of 1790, Trinity House orchestrated a campaign to find someone who would establish a lighthouse near Land's End. This information came to the attention of naval officer Lieutenant Henry Smith, who convinced the Corporation that his money and local knowledge would make the Longships light a profitable venture. On 8 October 1791, Trinity House issued Smith with a lease for the Longships project, together with the right to erect a lighthouse on Wolf Rock. But during 1792, Smith realised that the chances of establishing a light on the Wolf Rock was very remote, whilst on the Longships he thought it would be more profitable just to construct a beacon. Within 12 months the project was doomed to failure. Temporarily admitting defeat, he surrendered his lease to Trinity House.

Refusing to be beaten, Lieutenant Smith paid for the services of the architect Samuel Wyatt to carry out a survey to establish the best site for a lighthouse on the Longships reef. An agreement was reached between the Corporation and Smith that if a lighthouse was built on the Great Carnvroaz Rock, the largest outcrop of the Longships reef, they would grant him a lease. This lease was for 50 years at an annual rent of £100, with the authority to collect a compulsory levy for its upkeep of one penny sterling per ton from shipping that passed the light. Any profits from the venture would be retained by Lieutenant Smith. This levy could not be imposed until the light was operational, so up to this time all the finances for the project had to be found by Smith.

The financial difficulties that had plagued Smith since he began the Longships venture finally caught up with him around the early part of 1800. At this time, his backers demanded their money back, along with the promised interest. This money had been loaned on the assurance that it would be repaid within 4 years of the Longships light being lit. With most of the money still outstanding, Smith was ordered to appear in front of the Court of Chancery.

The Longships Lighthouse 1893 31809A

This case resulted in Smith being sent to the notorious Fleet Prison in London, where he had to stay until the debt was cleared. Trinity House took over the management of the Longships lighthouse and paid all of the profits to the court; an allowance was given to support Smith's family, and the balance was used to pay off his debts.

In 1836 Trinity House was empowered by an Act of Parliament to purchase any remaining leases and all the privately-owned lighthouses; at this time the Elders of Trinity House must have wished they had not helped the luckless Lieutenant Smith and simply revoked the agreement. Based on profits made from the Longships light, the Corporation had to pay the Smith family £40,670 plus all the legal fees for the remaining 9 years of the lease. Strange as it may seem, no information has been found which shows if the money paid in compensation was used to buy the release of Lieutenant Smith - in fact, there are no records to show that he was ever released from prison.

In December 1873, the William Douglass-designed tower which exists today was first lit. While the present tower was being fitted out, the former squat tower collapsed into the sea after being pounded by tremendous waves. (This close-up shows the site of

the first tower). The end of the little lighthouse was very apt: it had taken the pounding from the Atlantic Ocean for 88 years, but it waited until the new tower was completed before saying farewell in style.

At 11.27pm on 9 November 1898, the keepers were amazed to find the merchant ship 'Blue Jacket' stranded on to the Longships reef right beside the lighthouse. As the sea rose and fell, the ship rocked up and down like a sea-saw. She was written off and sold for salvage. One of the tugs involved with the salvage operation ran on to the rocks below The Land's End Hotel and became a total wreck.

A shocking tragedy occurred on 8 May 1917 when one of the crew was killed. While Chris Nicholas was cleaning the glass of the lantern, he slipped and fell to his death at the base of the lighthouse. When he failed to arrive in the mess room for his break, the Principal Keeper went to find him. The following investigation clearly noted that the ladder being used by Nicholas had been clipped to the guttering and not to the iron guard rail provided for this purpose. The coroner returned a verdict of accidental death. As a tribute to this well-liked keeper, the landing is now known as Chris's Walk.

The Longships lighthouse can be seen from the Cornish coast; in the days before radio communication was available, the keepers used semaphore flags to send messages to their wives, who were living in the Trinity House cottages at Sennen Cove.

There was one occasion when the keepers assisted as look-outs in an attempt to find a group of children washed off the rocks below the Land's End Hotel, but they were never found. A year later, a Trinity House helicopter pilot dropped bunches of daffodils into the sea close to where the children had been lost.

On 14 October 1988, the Longships lighthouse was automated and the keepers left for the last time.

The Longships Lighthouse 1893 31809B

Pendeen Lighthouse

Pendeen, The Lighthouse c1950 S255005A

The remote north Cornwall village of Pendeen is close to St Just in Penwith. The view from the top of the cliffs at Pendeen is breath-taking, especially during the winter months. Atlantic rollers crash along the shore, sending spray nearly 150ft into the air. Lying a short distance off shore are the notorious Brisson Rocks, the Wra or Three Stone Oar reef, which have become known as North Cornwall's graveyard of ships.

The first recorded ship to be wrecked close to Pendeen was the Rotterdam steamer 'Naais' on 23 June 1857. When she broke apart, the local wrecking community flocked to the scene in order to plunder the large cargo of wine and spirits on board. Several people were seriously injured and 6 men killed after a battle with the local militia and coastguards. All of the crew from the 'Naais' reached the shore safely.

It was not until 1900 that a lighthouse was established at Pendeen, because the powers to be felt that the existing navigational lights along the coast were more than suitable. However, with the advent of steam powered vessels and quicker and straighter voyages, the area around St Just became a mariners' nightmare. Designed by Sir Thomas Matthews, the

Pendeen tower is just 33ft 6ins in height from its foundations to the gallery. On top was erected a massive 24ft 8in-high helical lantern. When the light was first lit on 26 September 1900, its beam could be seen from 22 nautical miles away on a clear night. The height of this light was set at 194ft above sea level.

In the first few years of the keepers taking up residence at Pendeen, the fresh air was used as an excuse for a sudden population explosion. This literally turned the station into a mini-village. One particular keeper raised 5 children, which brought the number of inhabitants to 10 children, 3 wives, 4 keepers, 2 dogs, 3 cats, 5 pigs, 3 goats, 2 ponies, about 30 chickens, and 3 geese that strutted around the station as if they owned the place. For some reason these geese disliked the Area Superintendent, Lieutenant Harold Reading, who had to be met by the keepers because the birds would not let him get off his horse.

Covering a plot of ground that was almost the same size as the operational station were 3 gardens formed at the rear of the lighthouse. A high rubble stone wall was built, behind which numerous tons of seaweed were buried under freshly-cultivated top soil. But the expected spectacular gardens failed to materialise. Even after many hours of digging, planting and weeding, it brought the most enthusiastic gardener into a state of despair. All that was produced were salt-happy weeds, coarse grass and potatoes the size of large peas. In an attempt to overcome this problem, the keepers decided to dig down deeper and to enrich the soil. But all they found under the topsoil was the rubble and rubbish left by the builders. The only option left was to fit suitable gates around the compound and unceremoniously hand over the gardens to the goats and pigs.

Pendeen, The Lighthouse c1950 S255005A
The large air fog horns similar to those at Lizard Point.

During World War I the keepers enlisted with the Army, but this left the station without anyone to look after the light. Trinity House employed several people from among those who were rejected for active military service. One of them had a wooden leg. Each time he tried to climb up the winding stairs inside the tower, the leather straps holding up the leg came undone, which meant that he had to clamber down the stairs to retrieve it. On numerous occasions the light was late being lit. Under the circumstances, Trinity House decided that this man was unsuitable to stand in for the keepers.

One dark night in March 1976, Principal Keeper

Ken Chapman was growing concerned about the late arrival of his Assistant, Terry Osborne. Osborne had a record of being very punctual, so this situation was unusual; also, his home was only a short distance away in Pendeen village. Nearly an hour passed before an extremely dazed Terry Osborne staggered into the Pendeen station. Blood was running down the side of his face from a deep gash in his head. At first Chapman thought his assistant had been attacked, but while his head wound was being bandaged the story unfolded. Terry had been riding his trusty sit-up-and-beg-type moped along the approach road towards the lighthouse, when suddenly a badger ran in front of him. The brakes locked, which catapulted the startled keeper into the air. After crashing down, Terry Osborne lay on the road for nearly half an hour before crawling to the lighthouse. After first aid had been administered, he was driven to the local hospital for a check-up. Three weeks later he was declared to be fit for work - one of his first jobs was the repairs to his moped. But what of the badger? Sad to say, it did not survive, so the keepers gave it a formal burial beside the approach road at a point now known as 'Osborne's Head'. Terry Osborne remained a valued member of staff for Trinity House until 1996, when he became redundant owing to the automation programme.

The Pendeen lighthouse was automated on 23 March 1995. Although the keepers have now left, its former Principal Keeper has stayed on as its attendant and lives on station. Also, the lighthouse has come under the protection of the Trevithick Trust, and is being preserved and utilised as a special tourist centre. Even now, with the introduction of Global Positioning Satellites and receiver and transmitter facilities installed at these automated stations, the Pendeen light will still keep flashing each night well into the 21st century. Without a doubt, this lighthouse has played a major role in providing one of the best-lit seaways in the world.

Godrevy Lighthouse

Godrevy Island, The Lighthouse 1890 24195

Godrevy Island is the closest and largest of a group of rocky outcrops located about 4 miles off shore from St Ives in Cornwall. Close by is the treacherous Stones reef; its notorious reputation for shipwrecks is only beaten by the Manacles near Falmouth.

One of the first recorded shipwrecks near Godrevy was on 30 January 1649, a date better known for the execution of Charles I. The 'Garland' was carrying all the clothes and treasured belongings of the King's son (later to be Charles II) to France. But a severe storm blew up, and in an attempt to shelter in St Ives harbour the ship ran aground on Godrevy Island. From a complement of 60 passengers and crew, only one man, a small boy and an Irish wolfhound survived.

As sea trade increased over the next 200 years, the Stones reef became known as north Cornwall's graveyard of ships. Strangely, the pleas for a light close to St Ives Bay were being ignored by those with the power to establish this desperately-needed navigational aid. By the late 18th century, St Ives had become a busy port: ship-building and fishing took place here, and vessels making regular voyages to the Continent and Mediterranean countries called in. Also, two thirds of its population processed over 2 million pilchards each year.

This area of Cornwall has a sad history of heartless wrecking communities, equalled only by the barbaric wreckers around Lizard Point and Land's End. On 14 April 1815, the Fishguard brigantine 'Neptune' was wrecked on Godrevy Island. When the ship broke up, the tide carried its cargo and the crew's belongings on to the beach close to St Ives. A short while after the first items were spotted by the local people, the beach seethed with an uncontrollable mob fighting each other for a share of the spoils. Even the bodies of the crew were stripped and robbed. When an exhausted

Godrevy Island, The Lighthouse c1960 G187031

half-naked survivor dragged himself on to the shore, he was beaten up when he tried to retrieve some of his clothes. This gang then threatened to hang him if he made any attempt to claim his right of salvage.

The growing catalogue of shipping disasters around the Stones reef and Godrevy Island between 1820-40 was openly blamed on the lack of a suitable navigation light. In most of the cases, the ship was lost with none of its crew ever being found. In this 20-year period, among the ships lost were the brigantines 'Bellona', 'Neptune II' and 'Perseverance', the sloops 'Lord Nelson', 'Margam', 'Mary Ann', 'Providence' and 'Unity', and also the majestic sloops 'Clipper' and 'Rival', as well as one smack named 'Gipsy'. In total 150 men and boys perished; most of these victims were buried in a mass grave in Gwithian churchyard.

In 1854 a public outcry followed the tragic loss of the 700-ton steamer 'Nile'. This 3-masted ship was owned by the British & Irish Steam Packet Company, and was launched in 1853 at Greenock. She was considered to be very modern for the time, for she had a screw propeller instead of the recognised paddle wheels. However, this vessel seemed to be burdened with bad luck. On 4 July 1854 a Cornish miner, who was on his way home from Liverpool, fell through the engine room skylight when a guard rail broke. A month later, the 'Nile' collided with the brigantine 'William & Anne' close to the Plymouth Breakwater. Although badly damaged, the 'Nile' managed to return to Plymouth harbour, but the brigantine sank within 15 minutes of the collision and took her captain to a watery grave.

By 26 November 1854, the 'Nile' was back in her home port of Liverpool after extensive repairs. Her master, Captain Moppet, grew increasingly anxious about the weather and the delays it caused his ship. Even with a

Godrevy Island, The Lighthouse c1960 G187032

north-westerly gale churning up the Irish Sea, Captain Moppet refused to be held up any longer, and on 28 November the 'Nile' left Liverpool. On the night of 30 November, the 'Nile' was spotted by the keepers on Lundy Island; she was clearly battling against heavy seas. On board at this time were 60 passengers and crew and a total of 400 tons of cargo. Over the next few hours, the 'Nile' was sailing dangerously off course; at 2.30am on 1 December she hit the Outer Stones Rocks, which pierced her port side like a sieve. She took on water so rapidly that no one had any chance to lower the lifeboats. Tragically, everyone on board perished.

Board of Trade insisted that careful consideration had to be given as to the location of the light, and also at this time the Board of Trade were not prepared to sanction a vast amount of money for this project. There were even suggestions that the light should be added to the top of the disused fortress-style gun emplacement on St Ives Point. One ship-builder even offered to provide a light-vessel at his own expense for 3 years, to prove that it was unnecessary to establish a masonry tower on Godrevy. He positioned this ship near the Stones reef, but during the next winter its anchor chain was snapped in a minor gale and the vessel was wrecked.

Godrevy Island, The Lighthouse 1890 24194

The loss of the 'Nile' became the prime reason for a light to be established near St Ives. Within 2 months of her loss, a total of 8 petitions with a total of 280 signatures from prominent ship owners and merchants were presented to Trinity House. Yet the

Trinity House responded to a communication from the Board of Trade by requesting permission to position a temporary light vessel near the Stones reef while the construction of the Godrevy lighthouse was in progress. To support this measure, the Corporation enclosed a petition from prominent shipowners and merchants from Hayle and St Ives. Dated 28 January 1857, the petition informed the Trinity House Board about various ships that had fallen foul of the Stones Reef during the previous 4 years.

These ships included the 'Maria', which hit the Stones at the beginning of January 1855 and had to be abandoned. Although her crew reached safety, she sank with the loss of all their possessions and the ship's cargo. It was stated that the crew of this ship had been extremely lucky, as they were rescued by a passing St Ives pilot boat. In February 1856, the 'Josephine' ran into the outer Stone Rock, but was towed into St Ives by a local salvage vessel. The following month, the 'Desdemona' hit the same rock and was brought into port 'in a badly sinking state'. Two days later, the 'Ernest' suffered a similar fate.

Yet during the summer of 1856, one vessel was lucky enough to remain intact after it was blown off course by a freak gale. This vessel was a St Ives deep sea fishing boat that ran on to the Outer Stones Rock on its return voyage from Ireland; on this occasion her crew braved the choppy seas, landed on the rock and pushed the ship off. Tragically, luck was not on the side of a French lugger in October 1856. During an overcast night, this ship ran onto the Stones reef and became a total loss. All of her 16 crewmen drowned, and their bodies were washed ashore near St Ives. But no identification could be formally made of this French ship, or of the 15 members of the crew. The only clue to the ship's country of origin was from some papers found in the coat pocket of one of the seamen. An investigation was carried out which discovered that this particular crewman had changed ship in Jersey, but no-one could verify which vessel he had joined. The most recent disaster was on 15 December 1856, when the 'Mount Charles' hit the Deeper Rock. This ship was a total loss. Everyone on board drowned because no-one could get close enough to rescue them.

After nearly 3 years of political wrangling, the Board of Trade finally sanctioned the Godrevy lighthouse on 12 April 1857. The powers that be insisted that Trinity House had to offer the contract out for tender from independent builders. The letter sent by the Board of Trade states: 'in sanctioning the proposed design (built of rubble stone and mortar), my Lords direct me to observe that it appears to them that the estimated cost of £8,500 is very great; and I am requested that you move the Elder Brethren to invite Tenders for the construction of the tower of the lighthouse, in the local newspapers of the neighbourhood of the lighthouse, as well as the London newspapers'.

By September 1857 the Corporation had processed all of the Godrevy tenders. Although the final quote had to be within the stipulated budget, Trinity House needed to ensure that the professionalism of the chosen contractor was of the highest calibre. For this reason the building company of Eva and Williams, from Helston in Cornwall, was awarded the contract. Thomas Eva was already well known by James Walker, because of his former position as Borough Surveyor for Helston. In 1846 he had assisted George Burrell, one of the engineers for Walker & Burges, with the modernisation of the Lizard Point lights. His partner, Thomas Williams, was the founder and master mason of the building firm; he had many years' experience of quarrying and of the construction of breakwaters and other harbour facilities.

At the end of December 1857, James Walker formally notified the building contractors to begin the Godrevy contract. To supervise the construction work, James Sutcliffe was appointed as the project's residential engineer. During most of 15 and 16 January 1858, this engineer assisted Thomas Eva and his partner Thomas Williams to load the St Ives sloop 'Providential' with provisions, stores and other materials that were needed to start the contract. This ship was owned by John Jenkin Quick, and would be the supply vessel throughout the project. The accommodation for the men on Godrevy Island was extremely basic and consisted of waxed canvas tents. To live on an island with virtually no protection from the weather can only be imagined. It was not until the following March that a wooden barrack was built.

James Walker designed the Godrevy tower in the

were tapered externally to the course of masonry below the gallery, where the tower was 19ft in diameter. After the 2ft-thick granite gallery stones were positioned, the completed tower was just over 56ft in height. The internal area of the lighthouse was about 14ft in diameter, and there were 4 levels above the ground floor entrance lobby. Each of the floors were

Godrevy Island, The Lighthouse c1960 G187030

typical octagonal style of this period. Rubble stone masonry quarried from the island was used to construct the lighthouse. It had a cavity wall design, and its external surface was plastered with sand and cement (stucco) rendering. Its foundation was excavated out of the sloping rock surface to a depth of 3ft, into which was formed the rubble stone and concrete footings. On this levelled base the first course of masonry was set at 21ft in diameter, with the walls nearly 4ft thick. As the tower was being built the walls

constructed nearly 2ft thick, with the rooms almost 10ft in height. Access from the ground floor to the lantern room was made by climbing a geometrical stone staircase edged with an iron balustrade. A similar ornate handrail was also erected around the perimeter of the gallery.

The lantern on the Godrevy tower was originally intended for the pile lighthouse built on the Bishop Rock off the Isles of Scilly. But due to a tremendous storm on 5 February 1850, the partly-finished tower was washed away. This Wilkins & Son lantern remained in its workshop in London until it was adapted for use on the Godrevy lighthouse. The cost for this adaptation was £3,401, which for this time was a considerable sum of money. Standing on a 4ft-high hollow cast iron pedestal base, this 14ft-diameter lantern had a glazed section that was 11ft in height, topped by a conical roof of iron rafters surfaced with copper sheeting. This roof was then surmounted by a ball finial ventilator with a lightning conductor and wind vane.

On 1 March 1859 the Godrevy light was lit for the first time. To maintain this rock-based station, there was a Principal Keeper and 2 Assistants. Their tours of duty were 2 months on and 1 month off. John Tremearne, the local agent for Trinity House, was responsible for ensuring that suitable boats were hired from St Ives to ferry supplies and carry out the relief for the keepers. In 1899 a telephone link was established with Godrevy Island by a 200-yard cable stretched from the mainland. Trinity House were caused a great deal of embarrassment when it found out that the telegraph pole had been erected on the mainland in the centre of a protected Bronze Age burial mound.

On Christmas Eve 1925, the senior keeper was taken seriously ill with bronchial difficulties. His companion was unable to make contact by telephone because the main cable had snapped in a gale some weeks earlier. After sending up distress rockets, the St Ives lifeboat 'James Stevens' came out and collected the ill keeper. Due to the rapid response of the lifeboat, no other keeper had come out as a relief, so the remaining keeper had to carry out all of the duties on his own. Within hours the lone keeper found that the island was completely enclosed in a thick blanket of fog; he had to maintain the foghorn and the light by himself. These horrendous conditions continued until 2 January 1926, when the lifeboat managed to bring out two relief keepers. When the keeper reached St Ives he was treated as a hero.

By 1932 the Cornwall mining industry had collapsed, and this brought about a dramatic fall in sea trade. Trinity House converted the Godrevy light to acetylene; On Thursday 9th August 1934 Godrevy became officially an unattached light, It was arranged locally that the light would be inspected every six months. It became one of the first Cornish lights to be automated. In 1976 Trinity House attempted to supply electricity to Godrevy, which was produced by a wind-driven generator. Six months later, the fan snapped owing to the high winds, and the project was

Trevose Lighthouse

Trevose Head, The Lighthouse 1931 84349

Without a doubt, Trevose Head could be called the Lizard Point of the Bristol Channel, considering its reputation as a maritime graveyard. It has also been the focal point for barbaric wrecking communities, only matched by the heartless acts of plundering by the people along the south coast of Cornwall. It is around the area of Trevose Head, stretching from Newquay to Padstow, that the notorious north Cornwall wrecking communities gained their savage reputation. The majority of those involved were either fishermen or tin miners, who supplemented their meagre incomes with the rich pickings from ships lost during the bleak winter months.

When considering the volume of vessels lost around this deadly area of Cornwall, it seems unbelievable that a maritime light was not established until the middle of the 19th century. Up to the advent of the Lloyds Shipping Register, very little was recorded about the lives and ships lost along this deadly coastline. However, there are numerous mass graves recorded in the local churchyards that provide a gruesome reminder of the hundreds of sailors who died between 1700 and 1800.

One of the worst recorded incidents occurred at 9.00pm on 7 January 1754, when the 250-ton brigantine 'Bordeaux Trader' was blown ashore in Watergate Bay. Within 2 hours her master, Captain L'Abadie and his crew were thrown off the ship by what he called 'a passel of Cornish barbarians'. These people were then followed by the local Justice of the Peace, John Williams, and 6 of his henchmen. Under the guise of protecting the ship, they forced the local inhabitants off the vessel. Then Williams gave orders for his men to plunder nearly £10,000 worth of raw silk. More of the local community began to surround the ship, and a large group started to swarm on board. John Williams ordered his men to shoot their muskets over the heads of the angry people in an attempt to frighten them off. But before a shot could be fired, the men were attacked and thrown into the sea. Even the mate from the 'Bordeaux Trader' was beaten senseless by John Williams as he tried to retrieve his personal possessions. For more than 3 hours nearly 50 uncontrollable wreckers stripped the ship of everything of value; when they left, they set the 'Bordeaux Trader' on fire.

Living in a cottage close to the slopes of Trevose Head around the late 18th century, Thomas Parsons earned himself the reputation of being one of the craftiest smugglers and wreckers in north Cornwall. Revenue men had tried for many years to catch this elusive Cornishman with his smuggled goods, but still he managed to avoid capture and to supply many of the local inns with the best French brandy. He is also reported to have tied a candle-burning lantern to the tail of his donkey to lure ships on to the rocks. During the late 18th century it was often the practise of religiously-orientated people to provide a light for ships seeking a safe haven in bad weather. The biggest worry for Thomas Parsons was that his livelihood would be ruined if an official light was established near his wrecking grounds.

Trevose Head, The Lighthouse from the Rear 1931 84347

Trevose Head, The Lighthouse c1960 P1081

The first petition for a navigational light near Trevose Head was made by Captain E P Penrose in August 1809. Trinity House objected by stating that this area did not warrant a light. Nearly 39 years later, the tragic number of lives and ships lost between Newquay and Padstow had reached epidemic proportions. During this period, Lord Richard Lomax died and left his estates, which included the harbour and pier in Newquay, to be managed by a Board of Trustees. For 2 years this ill-informed committee struggled financially to maintain the estates. Then in 1835 Joseph Treffry, a wealthy merchant in Newquay, made an offer to buy the harbour and its pier. This proposal was readily accepted by the impoverished Trustees, and over the next 5 years Treffry rebuilt the pier and provided better facilities in the harbour.

As a shrewd businessman, Treffry also realised the value of a light on Trevose Head, because it would greatly increase sea trade using either Newquay or Padstow. With substantial interests in both ports, he managed to obtain hundreds of signatures from ship owners and merchants for a petition to Trinity House. Realising that the light had to be considered as being mainly for shipping in general and not just for the local ports, he made sure that the majority of the signatures came from harbours such as Bristol, Swansea, Newport, Cardiff and Liverpool. Although this petition was supported by a great number of people, it took a further 8 years before any official action was taken to establish a light near Newquay.

In July 1843 the Trinity House Committee visited the various lighthouses around Cornwall and Devon on board the Corporation's tender 'Vestal'. During their tour, the Committee conducted a survey around Trevose Head to decide on the best location for a new light. On their return to the steamer the tide suddenly turned, making it difficult for the crew to row against the strong current. As the coxswain tried to keep the boat on course, the current pushed it under the bows of the steamer. Tragically, two Elder Brethren were drowned - the weight of their wet uniforms dragged them under the hull of the steamer.

To further substantiate the need for a lighthouse at Trevose Head, severe gales on 17 October 1843 raised public concern over the length of time the powers that be were taking with their decision to erect a light. On 17 and 18 October, numerous ships were wrecked or seriously damaged around the treacherous coastline between Newquay and Padstow. The Fishguard-registered brigantine 'Hope' was smashed to pieces under the cliff near Pentine Point with the loss of her crew of six. The schooner 'Ceres', bound for Wales, went aground on the Greenway Rocks and became a total wreck. Luckily, all her crew were rescued. The Padstow ship 'Letitia' became stranded on entering her home port. Although the ship was seriously damaged, her captain managed to refloat the 'Letitia' and put into harbour safely. One other ship, the 'Wilberforce', en route for Cardiff, was hit by exceptionally heavy seas which ripped her stern boat from its davits, then smashed it to pieces against the wheel house. One seaman was seriously injured during the incident.

Following the tremendous gales during October 1843, the Royal Cornwall Gazette reported that 'the losses occasioned by every succeeding severe gale of wind, shows the necessity of a lighthouse on Trevose Head to point out to mariners their situation, and prevent their getting into bays, from which they can seldom work out again'. Joseph Treffry's petition was

Trevose Head, The Lighthouse from the Front c1955 S461086

received by Trinity House at the beginning of February 1844, and a final decision was made to progress with the proposed project.

The Corporation sent James Walker, its consultant engineer, to carry out a survey at Trevose Head and to prepare the designs and estimates for presentation to the Board of Trade. By July 1844 the completed documents were given to the Board of Trade for approval. Even the land rights had been cleared by the Crown Agents, so the Corporation believed the necessary approval would be just a formality. By August 1844 the Trinity House Committee was confident that the Board of Trade would give its authorisation, so it sent out tenders for the building contract and posted a notification in the newspapers. By October the Corporation had accepted a quotation from the Plymouth-based building company of Jacob and Thomas Olver. But the Board of Trade delayed its decision until February 1845, and the contract was delayed until the following May.

Carefully following the meticulous designs of James Walker, Jacob and Thomas Olver began building the 87ft-high lighthouse on Trevose Head. Its construction consisted of a two-level circular tower with a cavity wall. The external masonry was erected using local stone with a granite facing. The internal skin was formed using 4in locally-made bricks. Its base above foundation level is 25ft in diameter and tapers to 19ft at the top. The walls at base

**Trevose Head, The Approach Road
to the Lighthouse 1931** 84346

level are 4ft thick and diminish to 2ft at the course of masonry below the cornice. At the top a flat-sided polygonal iron lantern with plate glass was erected; it was 14ft high, with a diameter of nearly 15ft. A third of the lantern's surface was blanked off with metal panels to prevent the light shining onto the land.

The layout of the Trevose buildings was an arc, with the tower positioned close to the edge of the cliff. Around the lighthouse were the keepers' cottages and stores. On top of the single-storey buildings there were distinctive black chimney stacks that extended about 8ft above the roof.

Just 18 months into the building contract, the work force had a grim experience of the barbaric local wrecking communities. On 23 October 1846 the 220-ton brigantine 'Samaritan', on a voyage to Constantinople, was wrecked at Bedruthan Steps, close to Trevose Head, causing the death of the master, Captain Thomas Davies, and 8 crew. As the ship was being battered to pieces by the horrendous waves, its cargo washed ashore. Amongst the goods on board were finely-printed cottons, silks and calicos. These were accompanied by barrels of wine and spirits, along with boxes containing expensive dresses, which came within easy reach of the wreckers.

Word of the 'Samaritan' soon reached the local residents living in the surrounding parishes, who began flocking in their hundreds to share in the rich harvest. It took the local militia and excise men 3 days to bring the looting of the merchant ship under control. The Royal Cornwall Gazette of 25 October 1846 reported that 'all those involved seemed oblivious to the threat of imprisonment in the notorious hard labour Bodmin gaol, as they openly carried away their booty in their horse and carts'. The paper also remarked that 'it was lamentable that there should be found amongst these miserable wretches, men who stand up in the pulpit to preach the word of God!'

But the 'Samaritan' saga did not end after the militia gained control. On hearing the horrific details, a local magistrate ordered that every property had to be searched. One search led to a local farmer hiding part of the booty under a bed, then making out that his wife was about to have a baby. It appears that the family doctor must have been involved, as he confirmed the farmer's story. Although the rest of the farmhouse and outbuildings were carefully searched, nothing was found. From a report issued by a Padstow magistrate, the same farmer made an excise man suspicious when he was seen carrying a small keg of spirits on his shoulder. However, as he walked towards his farm on a return trip from his hideaway, he spotted the Revenue Officer. Once out of sight in a bend along the road, the quick-thinking farmer lifted a loose gate-post; after dropping the barrel in the hole he calmly replaced the post, then walked away. Although the officer was sure that he had seen the farmer with the barrel, he had no evidence to prosecute the farmer.

On 1 December 1847, when the Trevose Head light was lit for the first time, it coincided with the release date for many of the wreckers who were jailed for the 'Samaritan' incident. Its beam was set at 129ft above sea level and was visible on a clear night for 20 nautical miles.

When the Board of Trade received the final accounts for the construction of the Trevose Head lighthouse, the cost was £7,332. If we compare this figure with a principal keeper's salary in 1847 of £65 per year, we can see that this was a considerable capital outlay.

Within 12 months the light at Trevose Head brought about a dramatic reduction in shipping incidents. From 1847 to 1900 there were only 20 ships lost, with most of these incidents due to bad weather or fog. Compared with the 50-year period prior to the erection of the light, the number of wrecks was less than half. Shipping records from 1850 to 1900 clearly show that the volume of vessels using the St George's and Bristol Channel had trebled. But some ships still fell foul of this treacherous stretch of water.

On 5 November 1849 the schooner 'Ocean' was lost with no survivors. In February 1850 the sloop 'Lord Duncan' was wrecked in Mawgan Porth with the loss of everyone on board, and in November 1858 the Quies islets claimed the two-masted ketch 'Chere'. Within 2 years of the loss of the 'Chere', the same group of rocks claimed the Teignmouth schooner 'True Blue' during fog. Even a local Padstow schooner, the 'Caroline', ran on to the Bull Rocks in fog on 11 October 1867, with the loss of her 18 crew.

During the autumn of 1911, Trinity House began an extensive modernisation programme at the Trevose Head lighthouse. This included substantial improvements to the keepers' quarters. The work also

Trevose Head, The Lighthouse and the Rayleigh Fog Horn 1931 84348

included the long-awaited fog system, which to date had taken nearly 81 years to materialise. The first item on the agenda was to build a house for the large fog horn. This massive unit was devised by Lord Rayleigh, the scientific officer for Trinity House. It lay on the roof of the house, and was 36ft long with an 18ft by 2ft rectangular trumpet. The trumpet was designed to maximise the spread of sound. To power the Trevose Head fog horn, two calorific steam engines were installed to drive a large air compressor. On 6 February 1913, the Trevose Head fog horn was officially brought into operation. The event was received with mixed feelings: the shipping industry was extremely pleased with its introduction, but this was not the case with many of the local residents. Trinity House had numerous letters complaining about the 'shocking noise'. According to one resident, she had to remove all the dishes from her Welsh dresser during foggy conditions - if she forgot, the noise vibrated the plates and cups on to the floor.

Six weeks into the Trevose Head modernisation programme, the lighthouse keepers reported the sight of a ghost ship. On 12 November the 78-ton schooner 'Mary Jane' ran aground near Watergate Bay. When the coastguards reached her, there was nobody on board. They found the ships log, but there was no indication as to what had happened. During the following morning, the captain and crew from the 'Mary Jane' were located safe and well on board the Glasgow collier 'Ruabon'. It was then revealed that during very high seas the small schooner had keeled over, and her captain ordered his crew to abandon ship. But the 'Mary Jane' was far more seaworthy than anyone expected: she had continued her lonely voyage after being abandoned near the Pendeen lighthouse.

In 1913 the light source at Trevose Head was changed to a Matthews oil-burning incandescent mantle lamp that was fuelled by vaporised paraffin. This fuel oil was stored in 2 large tanks that gravity-fed a smaller tank inside the base of the lighthouse. Attached to this tank was a hand-operated pump, which the keepers used to pressurise the paraffin. From here the vaporised paraffin was carried through a narrow copper tube to the incandescent mantle. The keeper would light a small container which held methylated spirits and place it under the retort of the lamp. This would then heat up the pressurised paraffin. When a white fuming gas rose through the mantle, a burning taper would be used to ignite the burner. This method effectively halved the consumption of paraffin previously used in the former multi-wick lamps. When lit, through its optics this lamp provided an intensity of about 160,000 candlepower. A ruby filter provided the Trevose light with its characteristic red beam every 5 seconds for a distance of 21 nautical miles.

When a ship is wrecked, it is very rare for its crew to reach land and telephone the emergency services to report the incident. But on 3 October 1963, the coaster 'Humbergate' capsized about 4 miles off Trevose Head lighthouse. With no warning of the impending disaster, there was never any chance to send out a distress call. Yet Captain George O'Brien and his 4 crew managed to reach their life raft safely. Instead of drifting with the tide, they were gently blown by the wind onto the beach at Porth Joke Cove. After dragging their raft further up the beach, Captain O'Brien and his crew walked to the nearest telephone box and reported the incident. Apparently the coastguard on duty thought it was someone wasting his time, and did not believe it was the captain of the 'Humbergate' on the other end of the telephone.

In December 1995, Trevose Head was automated. When the news was announced, the local people complained to Trinity House about the loss of the keepers; but there is still an on-station attendant keeper who maintains a marvellous fund of stories for anyone who visits.

Bull Point Lighthouse

Up to the early part of the 20th century, one of the busiest ports in North Devon was Ilfracombe. Its natural deep water harbour made it a prime haven between Bristol and St Ives. Prior to the late 19th century, the mariner relied on the small light which shone from the Chapel of St Nicholas, on Lantern Hill in Ilfracombe. This medieval light was originally lit by the priest to assist the fishermen into port. St Nicholas was officially classified as a maritime light until 1730. After that time it was only lit at night between September and April.

Bull Point, The Lighthouse 1890 22967

On 31 March 1848, the 350-ton London-registered barque 'Princess Royal' ran aground in Morte Bay. She was on her return voyage from Mauritius to Bristol with a cargo of rum and sugar when she ran into dense fog off Baggy Point. Her master misread the headland and altered course onto a bearing which he believed would take him clear of Bull Point. Instead, the Princess Royal ran into Barricane cove. The crew from the stricken 'Princess Royal' managed to scramble safely ashore, where a local resident took them to Mortehoe village. When the master and his

crew returned to the vessel the following morning it had been stripped of its cargo. Only two broken sacks of sugar remained in the hold. Although a magistrate ordered the Ilfracombe militia to search the houses around the area, none of the cargo was ever found. Four days after running aground, the barque was refloated on the high tide, but a short distance off shore she sank alongside the many other wrecks in Morte Bay.

By 1870 large convoys of ships were using the Bristol and St George's Channels. This dramatic rise in sea trade brought about a tragic increase in the number of ships being wrecked around North Devon. In 1875 Trinity House provided a light to cover the area between Hartland Point and Lynmouth. The original Bull Point tower stood 71ft from the cliff edge and was 30ft in height from foundation to gallery. On top was erected a massive helical lantern, which was 14ft in diameter and 14ft 6ins high. When the Bull Point light was first lit on 12 August 1879, its beam was set at 154ft above sea level and was visible on a clear night for 20 nautical miles. This building contract was carried out by Yeo & Sons of Bideford.

Although priority had been given to the erection of the Bull Point light, other members of the Yeo & Sons workforce were constructing the remaining buildings. In front of the tower a single-storey, gable-ended building was erected. It was 47ft long by 28ft wide and contained a workshop, engine room, air compressor and a fog siren. To one end of this building was constructed a large coke and wood store, which contained the fuel for the large calorific engines. To ventilate this building, pottery glazed vents were fitted to the front and rear walls, with a large cast iron smoke pipe taken through the roof. Projecting through the front portion of the roof were the dual horns of the fog siren. This Douglass-designed air-powered system gave three blasts every two minutes in quick succession and was audible for between 3 and 4 nautical miles.

Bull Point remained virtually unchanged in its method of operation until 1950, when a modernisation programme was carried out. This work involved connecting the station to a mains water supply and the removal of the original calorific engines. In their place two Lister diesel motors were installed to power the air compressor. Modernisation of the family quarters saw such items as flushing toilets and enamelled cast iron baths with running hot and cold water. For some reason, these changes seemed to be of particular interest to the North Devon Journal, which sent one of its reporters to investigate.

When one of the keepers was asked by this inquisitive reporter if it was the normal practice for the station to be without curtains, the keeper responded by saying that the location of the lighthouse did not warrant such luxuries, although shutters were available if required. The reporter continued to press for further information and asked the keeper what he thought about the new facilities being introduced to the family quarters. The keeper commented that he thought the new bathroom was an excellent idea, because now it would stop his wife from frightening the neighbours, as she used to before, when she used the old galvanised tub in the kitchen.

In 1972, problems arose at Bull Point when one of the keepers, standing in the engine room, felt the ground move under his feet. After running from the building, he saw that large cracks had formed beside the engine room. Within minutes, 50ft of the cliff face broke away and crashed into the sea. The engine room soon collapsed and fell over the cliff. (The photograph shows the tower and the fog house before the landslip). Trinity House contractors demolished the original lighthouse and engine room and built a

new structure to the rear of the keepers' dwellings. While this work was in progress, Trinity House took back its trellis-style tower that stood on Braunton Sands near Barnstaple. This tower was no longer in use as a lighthouse, but it did provide the local bird watchers with a very good observation platform. When the contract was completed, this tower never went back to Braunton Sands.

On 25 July 1975 the Deputy Master of Trinity House officially lit the new light for the first time. This was not a particularly happy time for the keepers still at Bull Point: the building work had also coincided with an automation programme, which meant that the traditional keepers had to leave the station. However, a visit to Bull Point will provide spectacular sea views and a chance to find out more about this important lighthouse.

Detail From The Lighthouse 1890 22967
Bull Point Tower & Fog House Prior to Landslip

Lynmouth Foreland Lighthouse

On the edge of Exmoor close to the Somerset border lies the hilltop village of Lynton; its steep narrow winding road leads to the small fishing village of Lynmouth. In 1952 Lynmouth was the scene of a devastating flood, which saw a massive volume of water carrying boulders the size of small houses crashing down on to this peaceful village. Many lives were lost during this tragic event, but the 18th-century quay and fishermen's cottages survived.

There is a spectacular cliff top walk to Lynmouth Foreland along the path leading from the old inn near Countisbury. This very long and impressive route across the headland winds its way around the cliffs to the lighthouse. Although officially classified as being in north Devon, this station is also on the border of Somerset. Here the rugged trail is about 460ft above sea level, and there are breath-taking views

Countisbury Lynmouth Foreland Lighthouse 1911 63876

of the sea below. The grass gradually disappears as the track opens up to a well-worn footpath along the side of the sloping cliff. After a walk of about two miles, the track starts its descent to the lighthouse on Lynmouth Point, which is well below the headland.

Sir Thomas Matthews designed the Lynmouth Foreland lighthouse for Trinity House in 1897, but there were numerous political problems to be overcome before it could be built. Its location is about 20 miles to the east of the Bull Point lighthouse. It was not until 1899 that the project was given the authority to proceed. The contract was awarded to the local Lynton building contractors Jones Brothers Ltd. The Foreland site was in an extremely bleak and rugged location, with sloping cliffs that rose to over 500ft above sea level. Access to the site was virtually non-

existent, so one of the first priorities for Jones Brothers was to establish a roadway. Sections of this track had to be cut out of solid rock, but all of the excavated rubble was then crushed and used for hard-core in the road. Until this road was completed, the builders erected a temporary cliff railway which they used to haul supplies and materials from the various ships.

Lynmouth Foreland station has its lantern level with the windows in the upper floor of the dwellings. Its tower is only 16ft in height; onto it was erected a 14ft-high Douglass helical lantern. Originally the light source was derived from a pressurised paraffin system, which was then magnified by a massive 3-ton optic. Because of its enormous weight, this assembly was floated in an annular tray filled with over half a ton of mercury. As this liquid metal is six times denser than water, it is possible for a small child to rotate the optic with ease. Below the lantern room floor was a hollow cast iron stanchion, positioned centrally to the optical assembly. A heavy weight descended inside this pipe to power the clockwork drive mechanism which rotated the optic.

On 20 September 1900, the Lynmouth Foreland light was lit for the first time, with its beam set at nearly 220ft above sea level. Its visible range for shipping was about 26 nautical miles. In 1975 the station was connected to the mains electricity supply. It was also fitted with a radio direction transmitter which had a range of about 5 nautical miles. In 1994 Lynmouth Foreland was automated, and the keepers left the station. It is now monitored and controlled from the Trinity House Operations Control Centre in Harwich, Essex.

Burnham-on-Sea Lighthouse

Better known for its bucket and spade beaches, Burnham-on-Sea became a favourite Victorian holiday resort. Apart from the marvellous beaches, there is also a medieval church which was built upon the sand and now has a spectacular leaning tower. On the Esplanade at the junction of Regent Street is one of the town's earliest buildings, the Clarence Hotel, which was built in around 1796. Edwardian visitors to Burnham-on-Sea would crowd around a magnificent bandstand on the sea front. The bandstand was erected to commemorate the coronation of Edward VII and Queen Alexandra. This well-known meeting place was replaced by the Pavilion in 1911.

The Burnham or Bridgwater Bay lighthouse was established in 1832 and built to the designs of James Walker. The tower was built from locally-made bricks by a small construction company based in Bridgwater. The project started on 19 March 1831, and by Christmas the same year the majority of the tower was built. The severe winter storms hampered the project, but then good weather allowed the builders to complete the lighthouse on 10 September 1832. Its light is shown from 91ft above sea level. Its fixed light, visible for nearly 20 nautical miles, was only shown from the front of the tower; the rear was built in masonry.

There was also an eccentric-looking square-shaped low lighthouse, which stood on piles at the water's edge. When the high light was fully operational, the keepers took it in turns to stay overnight in the low

Burnham-on-Sea or Bridgwater Bay Lighthouse 1887 20086

tower. The location of these lighthouses was essential for shipping by night and by day: the ships had to navigate through the narrow channel by using the lighthouses as reference points. In 1884 a second red fixed light was added over the sand bar close to the station. Also at this time the main light was upgraded to an 60-second occulting beam.

For years, the only reasonable way to visit Burnham-on-Sea was by train, which would frequently stop at the Highbridge station on its way to Taunton and Bristol. Somerset and Dorset Railways opened the Highbridge station in 1854, and at the turn of the century it was one of the busiest stops along this line. This was mainly owing to the large quantity of dairy produce, especially milk churns, which were distributed by railway throughout the area. Throughout the summer months, holiday-makers literally trebled the local population during the first week following the end of the school term.

During the time that the high light was manned, it became one of the keepers' favourite stations because it was established in a town. (Southwold and Withernsea were also popular for the same reason). This meant that most of the keepers became very much involved with the local people.

The Burnham light was automated in the 1980s, when the keepers left for the last time. Today it is controlled and monitored from the Trinity House Depot in Harwich, Essex. It is still a major tourist attraction.

Originally Burnham-on-Sea had a brief spell when it had its own lifeboat, but this changed in 1882 when the region was brought under a new station established at Weston-super-Mare further along the coast. This followed a mass of petitions from the local people. Yet over the subsequent 84 years its operation appears to have been very uneventful; records of this period are few, until an inshore lifeboat was sent to Weston-super-Mare in 1966. However, on 10 April

Burnham-on-Sea
The Lighthouse, Rear Entrance 1918 68581

1969 the Barry Dock lifeboat (ON 806) was stationed at Weston-super-Mare to cover a necessary relief. Just 2 days later the area was hit by a tremendous storm, which broke the lifeboat from her moorings. She became a total loss. Luckily no one was on board at the time. A second inshore lifeboat (ON 961) was sent to the station, but it was then decided by the RNLI not to re-station another conventional lifeboat at Weston-super-Mare. A D-class lifeboat arrived in May 1966 to be replaced three years later by a new D-class lifeboat in April 1969.

West Usk Lighthouse

In 1821 James Walker designed and built his first lighthouse for Trinity House. In total contrast to the recognised style of lighthouses, the West Usk station's lantern room was built on top of a large circular dwelling. There is only one other station in the British Isles built with a large round keepers' quarters, and that is at Dungeness.

This area of Wales, where the Severn and Usk run into the Bristol Channel, was originally an island. Since that time the land has been reclaimed. To one side of the lighthouse the tide (the second fastest in the world) comes crashing against the base of the building.

The West Usk lighthouse was established by Trinity House as part of a chain of lights around the Bristol Channel. Its walls are over 2ft thick, and there are wedge-shaped rooms on both floors. Its actual light was recorded at being just 30ft above sea level. Its main purpose was to show a navigational reference with a bright white light to cover the Bristol Channel, and to assist shipping into Newport or further on to Swansea. A red sector light was also added to cover the Welsh grounds and Welsh Hook. Its main claim to fame is its architectural value. During the time that this station was manned, it is believed that three keepers, their wives and seven children lived in the dwelling. West Usk lighthouse was decommissioned in 1922.

This Grade II listed building was in a very poor condition when Frank and Danielle Sheahan purchased it in 1990. Frank Sheahan had previously worked for a major record company before he embarked on ten years of hard work restoring the derelict lighthouse. It is now a very romantic place to have a secluded weekend break. It has a wonderful sense of isolation, with only the wind howling outside and the sea crashing on to the rocks below.

When we consider the original sparse accommodation for the keepers, the West Usk lighthouse now provides a luxurious contrast. The beautifully-decorated bedrooms each have a unique view from the window. Without a doubt, a lot of love and dedication has been employed by Frank and Danielle Sheahan throughout this wonderful restoration venture. From a slate-paved hallway a spiral stair rises to the bedrooms. Above this is a flat roof, where you can enjoy the spectacular sunset or sit and watch the ships go by. Many of the original features have been preserved, including the indoor well that collected the rainwater. After many years of hard and dedicated work, the Sheahans have brought the West Usk lighthouse back to its former beauty; but it does need a continual flow of visitors to ensure that it stays alive. When we consider how long ago this lighthouse was established, its sturdy design stands as a memorial to James Walker and the men who built it.

Newport, West Usk Lighthouse 1910 62517

Mumbles Lighthouse

It is known that before lighthouses were built around the Bristol Channel, it was a tradition for local harbour pilots to light fire beacons on the Mumbles headland. The oldest family of Swansea pilots were the Williams, who religiously lit a fire every time a ship came into view.

The first mention of the Swansea Harbour Trustees' preparations to carry out the building of the Mumbles lighthouse was at their meeting on 5 September 1791. They also discussed the final section of the Harbour Act 1791, which allowed the Trustees to collect a levy from shipping at a rate of one farthing per ton; all vessels lying within 200 yards of the proposed new pier would have to pay one penny per ton. For whatever reason, the Trustees decided not to build the pier. On 7 November 1791, Thomas Morgan, the Chairman of the Trustees, asked the Duke of Beaufort for permission to erect the Mumbles lighthouse on his land. When this was formally granted, a letter was sent to Trinity House asking for its authority to exhibit a light in accordance with the

Corporations Charter. The Charter stipulated that Trinity House had the authority to decide on the location, necessity and suitable recognition on Admiralty and other merchant shipping charts. Without their sanction, a lighthouse could not be established. To implement this agreement with the Corporation, a lease would be issued and a nominal rent charged that would go towards the Trinity House Charities. At a subsequent meeting between the Corporation of Trinity House and the representatives of the Swansea Harbour Trustees, a formal lease for 99 years at an annual rent of £5 was agreed for the authority to display a light on the Outer Mumbles Headland.

Thomas Molineux, the surveyor for Swansea Harbour, presented the Trustees with a sketch of his proposed lighthouse on 7 May 1792. Just 18 days later, the Swansea Trustees accepted the design and estimate for the project. The price agreed was £315, and the contract was to be completed by 30 September 1793. Apparently Trinity House made no comment or even found fault with the design, as long as the proposed lighthouse was still positioned as agreed.

As a means for off-setting some of the financial risk, Thomas Molineux formed a partnership with a Mr Spencer and the construction of the Mumbles lighthouse began at the end of July 1792. The design put forward by Thomas Molineux was a cone-shaped stone tower, 50ft high with a battlemented top. This tower would be 25ft in diameter at its base, and taper to 20ft at the top. The walls were 4ft thick at first, and then diminished to 2ft near the floor of the coal brazier. A brick dome was built to support an iron coal grate, which was surrounded by an iron balustrade. In the original designs, a stone spiral

Mumbles Head, The Lighthouse and the Old Telegraph Station 1893 32731

staircase, 30ins wide, was to be built into the internal faces of the walls, with wooden floors positioned at equal levels.

However, the project proved to be a failure. Of the men employed only two were masons; the rest had no idea how to set even a brick in place. On 4 October 1792, the partly finished tower collapsed. This was a big disappointment for the Swansea Harbour Trustees, who over the past 12 months had repeatedly queried the cost of the lighthouse. Before he was formally dismissed from his contract, Thomas Molineux resigned. This allowed the Trustees to obtain the services of architect William Jernegan.

By June 1793, William Jernegan had started building another Mumbles lighthouse. The Mumbles Headland finally showed off its coal-fired light on 1 May 1794. Its first keeper was a John Walker, who had to travel from Swansea each night to tend the light. He had expected the keeper's dwelling to be ready when the light was first lit, but for some reason the cottage was not completed until nearly a year later.

When the cost of providing the coal proved far more expensive than expected, the Swansea Harbour Board decided to install some oil-burning lamps. It took the Board nearly two years to get permission by an Act of Parliament, which made the Mumbles light the last station in the British Isles to use coal. A small ceremony was provided by the Harbour Board when the new oil lamps were brought into service. In the Swansea Harbour Board minutes for 16 January 1799, it reads: 'that the treasurer do pay William Pritchet 10s 6d for Ale drunk at the Mumbles'. Research has shown that at that time a pewter mug containing just over a pint cost one half penny. Obviously they must have had quite a party!

By the summer of 1860, the War Department had finished the construction of the Mumbles Fort at a cost of £10,000. This limestone battery was erected in front of the lighthouse. At a meeting of the Swansea

Detail From 32731
Mumbles Fort with Cannon on Top

Harbour Trustees on 10 September 1861, the Chairman, Mr Starling Benson, voiced his concern about the new fort. He informed the Trustees that he had been well informed by a competent authority that owing to the close proximity of the guns, all the glass in the Mumbles lighthouse would be blown out when they were fired. This remark was later to be proved incorrect - when the cannons were fired for long range practice a few months after the meeting, no glass was broken. The keepers, however complained that the noise was deafening, and all the windows and doors shook every time a salvo was fired.

Between 1922–23 the Swansea Harbour Board sold its rights to the Mumbles lighthouse to the Great Western Railway Company. During World War II the fort beside the lighthouse was used as an anti-aircraft battery. It was not until 1969 that electricity was introduced to the Mumbles light; then in 1986 the station was automated. At this time, the British Transport Docks Board donated the Mumbles lighthouse to Trinity House. It is sad that this station has become so run down over the years; but help is at hand with a group of people who are planning to preserve this historic lighthouse.

South Stack Lighthouse

This is one of the most exceptional lighthouse stations belonging to Trinity House; it is situated near the north-west sector of Anglesey in Wales. It stands on a small islet known as the South Stack rock. Although this outcrop is about 106ft above sea level, it is dwarfed by its neighbour Holyhead Island. The island is faced by formidable sheer granite cliffs more than 400ft in height, and is separated from the South Stack rock by a 100ft chasm. Between these granite land masses the sea sweeps around the South Stack rock, and where it rejoins it erupts in a spectacular fashion.

The area around this part of Anglesey has been the scene of numerous tragic shipwrecks, mostly of vessels trading between Ireland and Wales during the

South Stack, The Lighthouse 1892 30299

late 18th century. In 1665 Sir John Coryton petitioned the Lords of the Privy Council for Trade for permission to be granted by Charles II to establish a light on South Stack rock. This caused a public outcry, especially from the ship-owners around Wales. When his petition was first presented, he suggested that 'one penny for each laden ton should be paid by English ships and double from Foreign', and in his papers he clearly stated that the Irish, Scottish and Welsh vessels were to be classified as foreign. Later, he agreed to amend his petition in favour of all ships in the British Isles.

Yet there was one further obstacle to overcome. This was Samuel Pepys, who at this time was an Elder Brother for Trinity House. He was strongly opposed to any privately-owned lighthouses, because none of the profits ever went towards the charitable interests of the mariner. He also felt that considering the volume of vessels that passed the South Stack rock during this period, the toll would prove to be an unwarranted financial burden on shipping. However, the situation changed by the end of the 18th century, when sea trade passing the South Stack rock had significantly increased. With this wealth of trade also came the tragic loss of ships along with their crews and cargoes. Trinity House applied for its own Royal Patent in August 1807, but it was not until January 1808 that permission was granted and the project started.

The South Stack lighthouse station was designed and built by Daniel Asher Alexander. Welsh quarrymen were employed to produce the masonry for the station out of the hard South Stack rock. Construction continued during the remainder of 1808, and continued through an extremely harsh winter into 1809, when the 92ft-high lighthouse was completed; it was lit for the first time on 9 February. Its light is recorded as being set at 197ft above the highest spring tide level. The main light was produced by Argand lamps and catoptric reflectors, and had a

recorded illumination of 19 nautical miles. When the keepers' quarters were completed during May 1809, the total cost of this part of the contract was nearly £12,000.

The most arduous task given to the stone-cutters and quarrymen was the formation of 400 steps carved out of the hard granite face of Holyhead Island. At the bottom of these steps a 100ft-long hemp cable was stretched across to the South Stack rock. With the use of a large basket, stores, equipment and keepers were hauled over to the rock. This system remained in service until 1828, when a 6ft-wide iron suspension bridge was built. At this time, no fog signal was needed because of the ever-present noise from hundreds of sea birds that nested around the rock.

In 1840, a unique way of showing the light followed complaints that the South Stack lighthouse was regularly hidden by heavy fog. A cliffside railway was established, and a light on a small trolley was fitted onto it. When fog covered the rock, the keepers would lower the trolley down the side of the cliff. Yet even with this very bright light ships were still being lost, although not in the epidemic proportions as before. It was important for ships under sail to be as far as possible out to sea during high winds or gales. However, on Tuesday 25 October 1859, during one of the most severe storms of the 19th century, a tragic shipping incident involving the 'Royal Charter' occurred.

As she crossed the Irish Sea towards Milford Haven, the steamship 'Royal Charter' was hit by tremendous waves and high winds, which blew her off course and into the South Stack rock. The keepers were powerless to help and could only watch in total disbelief as 500 people drowned. This incident was the worst of more than 200 others, where ships had been either blown ashore or floundered in the high seas. This event became known as the 'Royal Charter Gale'. On the same night as the tragedy occurred, one of the

South Stack, The Lighthouse 1892 30300

keepers was making his way across the iron bridge when he was hit on the head by a rock that had broken away from the cliff. Covered in blood, he tried to climb the steep path to the lighthouse, but collapsed a short distance from the bridge. He was not found until the early hours of the following morning. This unfortunate keeper died 3 weeks later from his horrendous injury.

In 1938, Trinity House installed generator sets and provided the South Stack with electricity. This system remained in service until the 1970s, when mains electricity was introduced. In 1964 a new aluminium suspension bridge was provided, and with it an oil pipeline with a duct for carrying the mains cable. On 12 September 1984 the keepers left the South Stack lighthouse following its automation.

Beaumaris Lighthouse

The Welsh island of Anglesey has an amazing history. It has what is claimed to be an unfinished masterpiece in the form of Beaumaris Castle. This mammoth building was begun in 1295 by the King's military architect, James of St George; it was the biggest and most ambitious venture he ever undertook, and money and materials ran out before the fortifications had reached their full height. Originally it was built as one of the 'iron ring' of North Wales castles by the English monarch Edward I as a means to impose his supremacy on the Welsh people.

One of the most impressive engineering feats undertaken during the early years of the 19th century was the building of the Menai Straits bridge. The Scottish civil engineer Thomas Telford (1757–1834) proved his versatility with the design and construction of this bridge from 1819 to 1826.

Coastal shipping making the passage up or down the western sea lanes must go round the island of Anglesey and because of this, several major lights were established. The Skerries was the first station to be built, with South Stack and Lynas Point following nearly a century later. The need for the Lynas Point lighthouse was established by the tragic loss of the 'Rothesay Castle' on Puffin Island at the entrance to the Menai Straits in 1830.

Before this tragic incident, Liverpool master pilots had already requested a navigational light on the shore at Black Point, or Trwyn Du, but no action was taken until late in the 1830s. In 1833 Trinity House commissioned James Walker to design and build a new tower on a low-lying rock surrounded by shingle beaches about half a mile south of Puffin Island. The tower is a circular granite structure with a castellated gallery. It stands 96ft high, and the light is set at 61ft above high water level. The base of this tower is in a step-like formation, which effectively breaks up the force of the sea into a mass of spray. Its fog signal system consisted of a large brass bell. Three black bands were painted on the tower to provide a positive daytime marker for shipping. By 1838 the Trwyn Du project was completed at a cost of £11,589.

Originally the Trwyn Du lighthouse was manned by two keepers, but in 1922 Trinity House converted the station to acetylene operation. With the use of this volatile gas, it was possible to do away with the constant presence of a keeper; the light was now self-operating, and its only requirement was for the gas cylinders to be changed every six months. This made Trwyn Du one of the first Trinity House lighthouses to be automated. Trwyn Du Lighthouse was converted to solar power in 1996. During this modernisation programme, Trinity House engineers also developed a unique operating mechanism to work the large fog bell.

The Trwyn Du or Beaumaris Lighthouse 1890 23155

New Brighton

New Brighton is situated on the extreme tip of the Wirral Peninsula, and is separated from the busy city and port of Liverpool by the River Mersey. The town is now a shadow of its former glory as a bustling, thriving seaside resort during the Victorian era. This was a period when thousands of hard-working Liverpudlians took their families on a much-needed break. These were also the days when building sand castles, watching Punch and Judy shows, searching for strange shells and swimming in the sea added up to the perfect holiday.

In 1683 the Liverpool Corporation erected a large post topped with a light and supported by a tripod of wooden legs on Perch Rock. It stood next to the fort, and became known as the Perch light. When foreign ships passed the Perch, they were charged sixpence for its upkeep, but the local vessels were exempt from this levy. Due to the frequent heavy seas and sudden squalls, this flimsy-looking structure was often washed away, and a boat had to be launched to recover it from Bootle Bay.

In February 1821, the pilot boat 'Liver' ran into the Perch during a heavy blanket of fog and carried it away. It took nearly 3 weeks to find the elusive structure. During this time, 4 vessels ran aground close to the fort. Heavy seas ripped the Perch from its site and washed it away in March 1824, and this time it was not recovered until the following December. The cost of repairing or replacing the Perch became extremely expensive, and so the Liverpool Corporation decided to build a more substantial lighthouse.

New Brighton, The Lighthouse 1892 30413

The architect and engineer Mr Foster was commissioned by the Liverpool Corporation to build a lighthouse for New Brighton. It was designed on the lines of Smeaton's Eddystone off Plymouth in Devon, and built from granite obtained from an Anglesey quarry by Tomkinson & Company. The granite is recorded as being 'the best in Wales'; it cost 1/6d a cubic foot. The Mayor of Liverpool, Thomas Littledale, laid the first foundation stone for the lighthouse on 8 June 1827. It was built to a height of 90ft above the rocks, and is considered to be a masterpiece of engineering skill.

Etna. This substance became rock-hard as it cured over the years. The first 45ft of the tower is solid granite. The hollow upper portion contains a spiral staircase that ascends to the keepers' quarters and then up to the lantern. Work was only possible at low tide; this meant that it took the builders 3 years to construct the lighthouse. In the first year, 10 men were stranded, after they failed to note the incoming tide. A thunderstorm erupted with torrential rain and with the sea extremely rough, no boat could get close enough to collect the men. For nearly 8 hours the men braved the horrendous weather conditions until

New Brighton, The Lighthouse, Low Tide 1887 20069

In a similar way as the Eddystone tower, each piece of granite was carved with dovetails which interlocked into the next section of masonry. On completion, the tower was coated with a layer of pulverised volcanic rock, known as 'puzzellani', which came from Mount

at last they were able to leave the partly-constructed tower.

The lantern was first lit on 1 March 1830; it consisted of two white flashes, followed by one red, with a range of 14 nautical miles. The light was recorded as being

77ft above sea level. Its revolving light was claimed to be the first of its kind in England. On completion, the total cost of the project was £27,500. The New Brighton lighthouse was converted to electrical operation in 1958, with power supplied through a cable brought underground from the mainland. During the short period that the New Brighton lighthouse was in active service, ships running aground became a rarity.

On 1 October 1973 the New Brighton lighthouse was discontinued: it was declared as being no longer necessary, because of the radar system operating in the river. A year later a local architect purchased the lighthouse for £100 on the understanding that he kept the structure in good condition. One of his first intended projects was to restore the lantern along with its light, but the river authorities objected because it would cause confusion to local shipping. Instead, the architect refurbished the lantern as a sun lounge to make it an added attraction for people wishing to stay there for a short holiday. It was originally advertised as the ideal place for newly-married couples to spend their honeymoon. The cost of this secluded venue would be £50 a day, including champagne and flowers.

Today, New Brighton lighthouse still has its wonderful sun lounge and a kitchen is provided in the former watch room below the lantern. On the first floor is the bathroom, with a shower and fully-fitted toilet facilities. There is a living room and a bedroom on the next two floors and even a television for anyone who gets bored with looking out to sea. Anyone wishing to stay in the New Brighton lighthouse has to be reasonably fit. A long ladder must to be obtained from the fort in order to reach the first of 15 iron rungs that provide access into the lighthouse. This entrance door is 25ft above the rock surface.

A visit to the Merseyside Maritime Museum provides a well-documented insight to the lives of the people who enjoyed the holiday resort of New Brighton. Its River Room takes the visitor back in time. Here we can explore the importance of the river, and how it has affected the lives of the Merseysiders.

This area was once at the heart of the slave trade, with a seemingly endless flow of African people being taken to America. This so-called legalised trading brought wealth to the region, but at the cost of thousands of lives. Crowded and chained into unseaworthy ships, many of these helpless people never reached their destination. Records show that during these slavery days the area of New Brighton was where various ship owners exercised and traded this human cargo.

In the museum there is a wonderful gallery which tells the story of holidays over the last 150 years. There is one special display that shows footage of holidays in New Brighton and the amazing swimwear that was worn during the 1950s. Memories rush back when we view the amazing collection of models, posters, leaflets and souvenirs that shows the popularity of this town and of Eastham.

The River Mersey has proved a challenge by acting as a barrier between the communities that have lived on either side of the water. Some form of ferry has crossed the Mersey since medieval times. One of the first to be recorded was provided by the monks at Birkenhead Priory. At this time they made the crossing in small boats. In 1815 the first steam ferries were introduced, and suitable landing stages were rapidly constructed in the 19th century. Ferries solved the problem for foot passengers, but the arrival of the car made people seek other ways to cross the Mersey. At the museum, its tunnel exhibition shows how Merseyside was developed for local transport systems, and how the riverside location of Liverpool was utilised. The Queensway Tunnel was completed in 1934; this tremendous engineering achievement was celebrated by 80,000 people doing a tunnel walk.

New Brighton, The Lighthouse, High Tide c1872 7886

Over the past few years, the allocation of much-needed funds from European grants has been awarded in the area, but bureaucracy and local politics has made any progress with the revitalisation of the town painfully slow. The aim of this project is to regenerate New Brighton as it was in the 19th and early part of the 20th century.

Fleetwood

Fleetwood is unique because it is the only town in the United Kingdom to possess three lighthouses. During the period between 1835-40, the wealthy Sir Peter Hesketh Fleetwood decided to develop his land and turn it into a new town. Permission was granted by the Crown, especially as his intention was to dredge a major portion of the Wyre river and its estuary channel. This would then allow the small port to expand, which would provide a lot of employment for this run-down area. Not only did this idea work, but it also saw the start of a regular ferry system that provided boats for people wishing to go to the Isle of Man, especially during the summer season.

To assist Sir Peter Fleetwood in his plans, the services of the well-known architect Decimus Burton were obtained. Decimus Burton (1800-1881) was an exceptional architect who was responsible for many of Fleetwood's early buildings. These included the North Euston Hotel, Fleetwood Town Hall (which today is the town's museum), St Peter's Church in Lord Street, the cottages at the rear of the Mount, the Mount Street houses (between Lord Street and Blakiston Street), and Queen's Terrace. Burton was also held in high esteem in London for his designs and practical assistance with buildings such the Hot House and Palm House at Kew Gardens. His best-known building is the Royal Botanic Gardens.

Within the space of two years, Burton had designed the whole town of Fleetwood, and allowed for the building of two spectacular lighthouses. These structures are actually located within the town itself and are still fully operational. The beam from the lower lighthouse is 30 ft above sea level and can be seen by shipping from a distance of 9 nautical miles. In the upper lighthouse, there are 107 steps and a 10ft ladder to climb in order to reach the lantern room, which is 90ft above sea level with a light that is visible from 13 nautical miles away.

When Decimus Burton put together his plans for the location of each of his lighthouses, a great deal of attention was given to the way the beams would be viewed by the mariner. Each of the lights compliment the other, and are positioned so that the upper light can be seen directly above the low light. If a master of a ship can see these lights as if they appear to be in one tower, then he knows that his vessel is safely in

Fleetwood, The High Lighthouse 1901 47079

the centre of the channel. These structures were situated at the north and south end of the wharf bank. Both are now considered to be of considerable architectural interest.

On completion of the Fleetwood promenade and the two lighthouses, Queen Victoria arrived to officiate at its opening ceremony. At this time the fuel source for the light was coal gas. However, because everybody used gas for either cooking or lighting, the pressure often dropped when demand was heavy - normally at around 6.00pm the street lights would dim for nearly an hour, until the local people had finished cooking their food. Queen Victoria unveiled a commemoration plaque, then formally declared the lighthouses officially lit, to an enthusiastic round of applause and the local band playing. Both lights proved to be extremely bright, but within 5 minutes the lower lighthouse dimmed and died. After the publicity surrounding these lights and their promised infallibility, this must have caused some embarrassment for Sir Peter. This problem continued for nearly 4 years, until the Gas Board provided a larger gas holder. Today these two lights are still in service and managed by the Fleetwood Harbour Trustees.

The third lighthouse is on the Wyre river; it was built in 1840 by Alexander Mitchell, a blind engineer from Ireland. It stands upon 7 screw piles sunk into the seabed at the northern edge of North Wharf, which is the sandbank that stretches from Fleetwood to the edge of Lune Deeps in Morecombe Bay. Before Alexander Mitchell became totally blind he had observed how an auger bit, used by a carpenter to bore holes into a piece of wood, could not be removed until it had gone all of the way through; to get the auger bit out before this, it had to be rotated in reverse. He experimented with much larger sections, similar to a ship's propeller, which were attached to long lengths of iron rods. His intention was to drive this pole into the soft mud in Dublin Harbour, so that he could tie his boat to a firm mooring. His idea soon caught on: after his design had been patented, hundreds of people used his new mooring poles. After Mitchell lost his sight, an associate put together his invention to the specifications Mitchell had given. In its turn, the Mitchell screw pile was born; it was nearly 5ft in diameter, with up to 30ft of iron pole attached to it. When a group of piles were driven into sand banks or mud and set into an octagon formation, a cast iron cabin could be erected on top. This method allowed for each pile to carry up to 64 tons in weight.

Unfortunately, Mitchell's historic lighthouse has fallen into a state of disrepair, with no-one interested in taking the responsibility for restoring and preserving such an important piece of early Victorian engineering. This seems even more regrettable because this type of structure is unique; it was one of the first screw pile lighthouses to be established in England.

Fleetwood
The High Lighthouse, The Lantern 1901 47079A

Berwick Lighthouse

Berwick sits at the mouth of the Tweed, a river famous for salmon fishing. The 2-mile walk around Berwick's magnificent Elizabethan walls are one of the best ways to enjoy the town, for from the walls there are exceptional views of the fine Georgian and Regency buildings and rugged cliffs. Afterwards, a walk through a wooded area towards the river reveals the town's famous swans and its historic bridges. This once heavily-fortified border town is at the most northern extremity of England. It is also midway on the Newcastle to Edinburgh railway line, and is the focal point for the roads leading out to the sparsely-populated regions of north Northumberland.

Not only did Berwick have a large fishing fleet during the 18th and 19th centuries, but it was one of the safest havens for ships sheltering from the unpredictable North Sea. Berwick also became a staging point for passenger vessels sailing further north into Scotland. This final step in any Scottish voyage up to the late 18th century was considered to be very perilous, especially with Scotland being devoid of any suitable navigational lights. This was soon to be rectified with the forming of the Northern Lighthouse Board and the relentless building programme implemented by the Stevenson family. During the early years of the 19th century, the thriving harbour had a massive breakwater built; much of the work force consisted of prisoners serving hard labour. Around 1810, there was a significant increase in predominantly coastal vessels carrying coal or limestone further north, which brought about a rapid expansion of Berwick-on-Tweed to allow the trains to be loaded directly from the ships. For this purpose it became necessary to establish a suitable navigational light.

The 44ft cast iron lighthouse which stands on the pier head was established in 1826; it provided a bright white fixed light for a visible distance of 11 nautical miles. From a small window set at 28ft above sea level a red sector light was displayed to warn of the location of the nearby Sand Bar. This light was originally produced by an oil-burning lamp and reflector, which was converted to coal gas at the beginning of the 20th century. Around the middle of the 1960s the light was electrified.

Berwick-on-Tweed, The Pier Lighthouse 1965 B305038

Tynemouth Lighthouse

Ship owners in Tyne and Wear around the middle of the 18th century realised that the safety of their vessels, cargoes and crews depended on the improvement of the hazardous river-mouth entrances to the harbours - yet these improvements took over 200 years to be completed. In 1730 the River Wear Commissioners finished their first project, which was the construction of the South Pier. This barrier protected the mouth of the river, and directed the tide onto the nearby shallow bar to form a deeper channel. To protect the pier from being rammed by shipping, a wooden lighthouse was erected on its extreme end, which also provided a marker for those entering the river. The North Pier was built between 1787 and 1802 by Jonathan Pickernell, the Commissioner's engineer. On this pier he also erected an octagonal stone tower which stood 76ft in height.

However, no sooner was one project finished, when the ship owners demanded even more improvements. In the 1840s and 1850s both piers and lighthouses had to be altered. The North Pier was lengthened, and by an incredible feat of ingenuity the octagonal lighthouse, weighing 334 tons, was moved bodily 450ft along the pier. The old wooden tower was replaced with a tall lighthouse built of wrought iron. This tower was taken down in 1983 and erected on the cliffs at Seaburn.

Ships built of iron or steel began increasing in size, and they therefore needed a greater depth of water. To achieve this, a 17-year project was begun in 1885: the construction of the 2,800ft-long Roker Pier outside the old North Pier. Its red and white granite lighthouse was opened in 1903. After the new south pier was started in 1890, the direction of the sea changed, so that the force of the waves wrecked the old piers. Pickernell's octagonal lighthouse had to be taken down and replaced with a lighter tower.

The Tyne Improvement Commission was not formed until 1851, but it immediately began ambitious engineering work at the river mouth. Its plans included the building of huge protective piers with lighthouses, and deepening the channel right up to Newcastle. But still more work had to be done, for ships were still missing the safe channel after passing the piers. A light was needed, and in 1882 Trinity House built a steel light on the groyne at South Shields.

Victorian engineers also improved the system of lighthouses, which helped ships to navigate along the north-east coast. In 1871 Souter Lighthouse was opened on Lizard Point between the rivers Tyne and Wear, and in 1898 St Mary's Lighthouse came into service between the rivers Tyne and Blyth. The Tynemouth Pier light is still in service, although it is fully automated now.

Tynemouth, The Lighthouse c1955   T142051

Seaham Lighthouse

Seaham, in County Durham, has a history which stretches back over 1200 years. The church of St Mary the Virgin, which stands on the cliffs near the edge of Seaham Dene, dates back to Anglo-Saxon times. In April 1814, the poet Lord Byron came to Seaham to win the hand of the talented Anne Isabella Milbanke, whom he had met just a month before. They were

harbour. By 1831, Lord Londonderry had constructed a railway line from the Rainton pits to his harbour at Seaham. However, the Rainton Colliery closed in 1896 and the Seaham line became redundant. The section of line to the harbour was transferred from the Londonderry collieries to the Hetton Colliery Company; a junction was created which allowed it to

Seaham, The Pier Lighthouse c1955 S287022

later married in Seaham Hall, where today there is a picturesque road lined with trees known as Lord Byron's Walk'. During the 1820s the Milbanke family sold their estate to Charles Stewart, the 3rd Marquess of Londonderry and his coal heiress wife, Frances Vane-Tempest. In 1828 the Londonderry family decided to construct a private harbour at Seaham. The shipping activity, combined with a coal-carrying railway, meant that the town grew along with the

ship coal from either Sunderland or Seaham Harbour. The line to Seaham Harbour was rarely used, so it was abandoned in around 1920. After a working life of 137 years, the Hetton Colliery Railway carried traffic for the last time on Wednesday, 9 September 1959, and dismantling began the next day. The last 90 feet of track was lifted at Hetton on November 20 1960.

In the early 1900s, the dock doubled in size with new quays, large curving piers and a lighthouse.

Seaham, The Lighthouse c1955 S287017

These all stand today in virtually their original condition. The lighthouse is a 58ft-high stone tower at the end of the pier, constructed so as to allow ships to come and go at all times of the tides. The light was first exhibited in 1843; it was set at 94ft above sea level. The visible distance on a clear night was recorded as being 14 nautical miles.

The commercial south dock area is overlooked by the Coastal Centre. When looking from the windows of this building, there is a wonderful view of vessels loading and discharging their cargoes. The majority of these goods come from Europe, the Baltic or the Mediterranean. There are no previously-arranged services, but ships do arrive on a fairly regular basis bringing various raw materials for British industry, including limestone, fertiliser, steel scrap, timber, chipboard and anthracite. This was not the original purpose of Seaham Harbour, which was established in 1828 solely for the exportation of coal (note the railway lines for coal trains in the photographs).

The Seaham Harbour Dock Company dates back to 1898, when it was established by Act of Parliament. A centenary celebration was held in the summer of 1998. Today this thriving harbour handles more tonnage than its neighbouring Port of Sunderland. The smaller North Dock was unable to accommodate the larger vessels that came with the age of steam and diesel; it is now used by inshore fishermen, who add their own personality to the scene. Crab and lobster pots are stacked on the quayside, which is a busy place when the cod, haddock, plaice and monkfish are being offloaded.

There are two estuaries, the Wear to the north and the Tees to the south, that radically affect the area. The Wear makes the greatest impact on the coastline at Seaham by depositing silt and other materials on its beaches. To the south, the beaches are slowly recovering from decades of dumping from the area's discontinued coal industry.

Hartlepool Lighthouse

Between 1836 and 1839, the Hartlepool Dock & Railway Company established a branch line from its harbour, with links to all of the major collieries. This line also extended to Moorsley and Rainton. The Rainton and Seaham line crossed the new railway at a point just south of Seaton, and a junction was created to enable the coal to be sent on the new line to Sunderland docks - this system effectively bypassed the need for trains to go to Seaham Harbour. In 1857, the Hartlepool Dock & Railway Company was taken over by the successful North Eastern Railway Company.

close to Hartlepool. Amongst those lost on that tragic night were 6 fishing boats owned by local people. In total, 15 fishermen lost their lives. It was later stated that had there been a light near the harbour, many of the vessels could have run to safety. After careful consideration, the Hartlepool Harbour Trust commissioned a local architect, Stephen Robinson, to design and build a lighthouse on the Heugh. This lighthouse was first lit in 1847; its beam was set at 84ft above sea level, and was visible on a clear night for 15 nautical miles. This pier light is still in service today.

Hartlepool, The Lighthouse 1892 30767

During the prosperous times of the Hartlepool Dock & Railway Company, the harbour expanded dramatically, with numerous coasters waiting off shore before entering the port to be loaded with coal. However, in the winter months of 1843 there was a tremendous storm which wrecked about 15 ships

In 1880 the NER constructed a branch from the Hartlepool and Sunderland line at Wellfield to Stockton via Wynyard Park. This created a connection between Wynyard and Seaham via Wellfield, Murton Junction and Ryhope. When this line first opened, the train not only carried vast amounts of coal, but also pulled a private carriage belonging to the Londonderry family - they owned the Seaham Colliery and the land on which the railway was established. In addition to the rent received for the use of his land, the 5th Marquess of Londonderry also had the right to halt any train anywhere along the line. This applied regardless of the inconvenience to other passengers.

The passenger service on the Hartlepool and Sunderland via Haswell was withdrawn on 9 June 1952. The line remained open for freight and minerals until the mid 1960s, when it was dismantled. The northern section from Hawthorn Shaft to Ryhope remained open until the closure of Murton colliery in 1991. This last segment was dismantled at the end of 1993. Hartlepool Harbour is slowly recovering from the many years of industrial abuse.

Hartlepool, The Lighthouse 1896 37506

The history of the lifeboat service at Hartlepool began at the Castle Eden Inn, where a group of local people held an informal meeting on 5 August 1802. That night a decision was made to commission George Hunter to build a lifeboat to serve the Port of Hartlepool. Among those at the meeting were the local fishermen who volunteered to man the boat. By February 1803, the new oar-powered boat had been built; however, its first rescue did not take place until 1815.

In 1841 the original lifeboat was replaced with a vessel constructed by the Hartlepool boatbuilder John Cambridge. Home for this 20-oar lifeboat, built for Tees Bay Lifeboat Association, was on the North Sands. Apart from North Sands, there were 2 other lifeboats serving Hartlepool Bay by 1842. One lifeboat served from West Harbour (or Middleton as it is known today), with the other stationed at Seaton Carew. On 9 February 1861 all of the lifeboats around Hartlepool became involved with a mammoth rescue operation. This serious incident occurred when nearly 100 ships were suddenly caught in the grip of one of the worst storms ever to hit the north-east. Between them, these lifeboats saved 40 lives and miraculously assisted 91 ships into port.

1857 saw the Royal National Lifeboat Institution taking over the Hartlepool lifeboats. These 3 rescue boats were stationed at the North Sands, Old Pier and Fish Quay. Within 30 years, funds had been raised by an organisation known as the Cyclists of the United Kingdom. To show its sincere gratitude for their dedicated contribution, the RNLI named this first self-righting lifeboat the 'Cyclist'. The 'Cyclist' was replaced by the 'Horatio Brand', which continued in service up to World War I. In 1924 the people of Hartlepool raised enough money to pay for its first motorised lifeboat. This boat was built at West Cowes on the Isle of Wight; she was a 45ft-long Watson-class vessel. She was launched by the Marchioness of Londonderry and named 'Elizabeth Newton'. She provided an excellent service until the outbreak of World War II. On July 21 1941, Her Royal Highness the Princess Royal came to Hartlepool and launched a new lifeboat. This vessel was another Watson-class lifeboat, and had one of the latest watertight engine compartments. This lifeboat was named the 'Princess Royal'.

During World War II, the 'A Hawkwood' ran aground 3 miles to the south of Hartlepool. On 16 January 1942 a strong easterly gale was blowing, with atrocious sea conditions and heavy snow. When the 'Princess Royal' arrived on the scene, the ship had broken in two, with her crew of 23 stranded on both sections of the vessel. The coxswain of the lifeboat could not manoeuvre his vessel close enough to take off the crewmen. The master of the 'A Hawkwood' informed the lifeboat that

Hartlepool, The Lighthouse 1914 67105

both parts of the ship were firmly wedged in place, so after serious consideration for the stranded men, the coxswain of the lifeboat decided to return at high water. When the lifeboat returned, the 'A Hawkwood' was still in shallow water, which made it hard for the lifeboat to go alongside. However, with great skill Coxswain M Bennison manoeuvred the lifeboat alongside the bow section of the ship and rescued 5 crew. The 'Princess Royal' returned to the scene and tried to rescue the remaining crewmen on the stern section of the ship, but every attempt to float a line to the ship failed. This forced Coxswain Bennison to return to Hartlepool to obtain a rocket launcher. Just as the 'Princess Royal' was about to embark on her 4th trip, Coxswain Bennison received a radio message that the coastguards had managed to rescue all of the crew from the shore by breeches buoy.

The 'Princess Royal' remained in service until 28 April 1968, when the RNLI decided that Hartlepool no longer needed a Watson-class lifeboat and could

easily be covered by an inshore rescue craft. The former crews felt that this was the demise of their tradition - people like policemen, yachtsmen and even canoeists would form a new era of lifeboat men. Yet during the period since this choice has been made, numerous lives have been saved by this fast and manoeuvrable inshore rescue boat.

In June 1972 the 'B 503', a new Atlantic 21-class lifeboat, was stationed at Hartlepool. Two years later she was replaced by the 'Guide Friendship III', named after the Girl Guide Organisation, which had raised the funds for her. Her first major rescue was in Tees Bay, involving a ship that had a serious fire in its engine room following an explosion. This event led the RNLI to provide Hartlepool with a new offshore lifeboat. The Scouting Association provided the funds (totalling £100,000) for a Waveny-class lifeboat suitably named the 'Scout'. She is a 44ft steel-hulled, self-righting lifeboat with 5 crew, capable of carrying 12 survivors. She was launched by Her Majesty Queen Elizabeth at Hartlepool on 14 July 1977. This was the first time a monarch had officiated at a lifeboat dedication.

On 9 November 1985, the Dutch coaster 'N V Anne' ran aground on the Longscar Rock during a tremendous north-easterly gale, with the sea breaking in 20ft-high waves. Coxswain Robbie Maiden took the 'Scout' out to rescue the crew of the coaster. With the sea continually breaking over the lifeboat, the only way to get the crew off the coaster was haul them aboard as the lifeboat came beside the ship. Although this was a very tricky manoeuvre, the 'Scout' made 4 runs and successfully took off one man each time.

In September 1986, 'Friendship III' was replaced by the 'Burton Brewer' - the funds were raised by the people of Burton-on-Trent. Along with the 'Scout', this lifeboat still provides an important service at both the Hartlepool and Tees ports.

Whitby, East Pier Lighthouse

Whitby, East Pier Lighthouse 1891 28857A

High Yorkshire cliffs and fine beaches extend to Ravenscar around Robin Hood's Bay from Whitby; the area is very popular with holidaymakers. The historical port of Whitby is still the base for a large fishing fleet, and it was from here that Captain Cook set out in the 'Endeavour' in 1768 on his voyage of discovery to Australia.

Whitby has a dredger that works daily during the summer months to keep the River Esk free from silt. This is to ensure that the trawlers and smaller craft have a clear passage to their berths. The marina was built in 1979, and has moorings for 200 vessels.

While the construction of the breakwaters at Whitby were under way in 1831, it was decided to erect two pier head lights. Francis Pickernell, engineer to the Whitby Harbour Trustees, was commissioned to design these structures; however, lack of funds delayed the construction of the east pier light until 1855.

The 83ft-high lighthouse on the extreme point of the west pier, beside the River Esk, was manually operated. It only came into service when a ship was due to arrive and it provided a positive guide to a ship's master that it was safe to enter the harbour.

On other occasions, this light was only operational from 2 hours before high tide to 2 hours after low tide. The light itself was coloured green, and had a visible range of only 5 nautical miles. In daylight hours a black ball was hoisted up to the top of the lighthouse. This light came into service in 1835. It is now open to the public (During the summer months) and offers breathtaking views on reaching the gallery.

The lighthouse on the east side of the River Esk is 54ft high and showed either a red or a green light. If the red light could be seen, then the approaching vessel was entering the harbour on an unsafe course. Its illumination was visible for nearly 8 nautical miles; it was first lit on 19 May 1858. This lighthouse was discontinued in 1890, and a red light was established on the nearby church steps. These two towers are very distinctive in design, and are considered to be of great historical interest.

Trinity House built the present James Walker-designed Whitby lighthouse in 1858 on Ling Hill, close to the harbour. When this new light was lit, its beam was set at 239ft above sea level and was visible on a clear night for 18 nautical miles.

At 10.30am on 19 January 1881 the Harbour Master at Whitby, Captain Robert Gibson, received a telegram to inform him about the local brigantine 'Visitor', which had sunk off Robin Hood's Bay. Her

Whitby, West Pier Lighthouse 1891 28857B

crew had taken to a lifeboat, but because of very heavy seas they had been forced to drop anchor. Around Whitby the weather was atrocious, with extremely high winds and the sea rolling inshore at a terrifying pace. These conditions made it impossible for the Whitby lifeboat to be launched. The only alternative was for the crew to haul the 'Robert Whitworth' lifeboat 6 miles overland to Robin Hood's Bay and launch it from there. There had been several days of heavy snowfall, so this was an extremely difficult task. The route went along very narrow roads, then across the moorland and through 7ft-deep snowdrifts. To help the Whitby lifeboat crew, about 60 men used shovels to clear the snow from the roads. A large team of horses were hitched to the lifeboat carriage to haul the Robert Whitworth to Robin Hood's Bay. Within an hour the word had reached the rest of the Whitby community, and eventually nearly 200 men were helping with the snow clearance. As this procession passed a local farm, the owner loaned his horses to the lifeboat crew. This brought the number of horses hauling the carriage to 18. A message was relayed by a man on horseback to Robin Hood's Bay, where the men began clearing a passage towards the approaching lifeboat. Just 2 hours later, this terrific team effort saw the lifeboat descending the very steep hill into the village.

Although the lifeboat crew were close to exhaustion, they manned their boat and set out to rescue the stranded sailors. Before they could reach the survivors, 6 boat oars and the steering were smashed to pieces by a heavy wave, which forced them back to the beach. Whilst the oars were being replaced, Coxswain Henry Freeman asked for volunteers to double up on the oars. With 18 men on board, the 'Robert Whitworth' set out towards the stranded crew of the 'Visitor'. After an hour and a half the lifeboat managed to reach the 6 sailors in the small boat and by 4.00pm the lifeboat had returned to Robin Hood's Bay. All of the crew needed medical attention along with some of the lifeboat men.

On 29 October 1914 the 7,400 ton hospital ship 'Rohilla' with 229 people on board left Queensferry for Dunkirk. At 4.00am on 30 October she ran onto the rocks at Saltwick Nab, about a mile south of Whitby. Weather conditions were atrocious, which made it impossible to launch the Whitby No 1 lifeboat. Instead, at 7.00am the 'John Fielden' was hauled across the beach and launched. Despite the terrible conditions, this rowing boat reached the wreck and rescued 5 nurses and 12 men. Although exhausted, the lifeboat crew returned to the ship and collected another 18 men; during this trip the 'John Fielden' was thrown against the side of the ship and badly damaged. It was then decided to use the Upgang lifeboat, which had to be lowered down the vertical face of the cliffs. But the very rough seas washed the vessel against the rocks, so the attempt was aborted.

Several telephone calls were made to the Scarborough and the Teesmouth lifeboat stations asking for help. The 'Queensbury' from Scarborough was towed by a trawler to Saltwick Nab, but by 6.00pm it was pitch dark, which made it impossible for any rescue attempt to be made. After the

'Queensbury' had waited for nearly 18 hours, the high seas forced her to return to Scarborough. Another attempt was made by the motorised Teesmouth lifeboat 'Bradford IV', but it was necessary to make a 22-mile journey to reach the wreck. In the attempt she was seriously damaged by an enormous wave, and had to be rescued by a tug. At 7.00am on Saturday 31 October 1914 the 'Robert and Mary Ellis' was launched into the harbour. The intention of Coxswain Thomas Langlands was to take her out to sea and wait for the steam trawler 'Mayfly' which would be towing her out to the wreck. But she only managed get about half a mile off shore, and by 9.00am she had to return to Whitby.

The Upgang lifeboat 'William Riley' was the next lifeboat to be launched, but after an hour of fighting against the atrocious sea conditions Coxswain Robinson and his exhausted crew aborted the attempt. One of the tugs tried to see how close it could get to the stricken 'Rohilla', but the waves nearly capsized it. It was finally decided that only a motorised lifeboat would be able to make any rescue attempt. The nearest suitable vessel was the 'Henry Vernon', stationed at Tynemouth, 44 miles to the north. At 4.15pm on 31 October the 'Henry Vernon' left Tynemouth under the control of Coxswain Robert Smith. Due to horrendous weather conditions, she took nearly 8 hours to reach Whitby. At 6.30am on 1 November she set out from Whitby; within 2 hours she had managed to rescue 40 men, before two huge waves crashed over her and the stricken 'Rohilla'. As if by a miracle, the 'Henry Vernon' recovered and rescued an additional 10 men from the wreck. From the 229 people on board the 'Rohilla', 84 were lost. Several of those involved in the rescue attempts received RNLI medals.

Whitby lighthouse was automated in 1992; it is monitored and controlled via telemetry link from the Trinity House Operations Control Centre at Harwich.

Withernsea Lighthouse

During the latter part of the 19th century, ship owners petitioned Trinity House for a light which would cover the area between Spurn Point and Flamborough Head. For many years, this area of water had become a graveyard for shipping, especially for vessels under steam. It was a known fact that ships under sail always stayed further from the coastline, mostly because of their zigzag courses; however, steam ships made faster and much straighter voyages, and travelled closer to the land. For this reason the shipping industry demanded that the lights had a brighter illumination and could be easily recognised from a greater distance.

When the petition was investigated, it was noted that in 1888 seven ships had been lost close to Withernsea during a single storm. A year later, 4 more coasters had run aground during heavy weather. Trinity House then acted upon this survey, and agreed to establish a light at Withernsea. Yet the Board of Trade investigated every objection to the project, especially from the local people, who were concerned

about the tower having to be built in the town. It took nearly 2 years before Trinity House could begin to erect the 127ft-high octagonal Withernsea lighthouse. Its light was set at a majestic 138ft above sea level and was lit for the first time on 22 September 1892, with its beam visible by shipping from 20 nautical miles away.

When this famous lighthouse was discontinued in 1976, the local people decided that their historical lighthouse should still have a major role to play in the community. In 1987 the Withernsea people restored the tower and converted it into a museum. It was not only to contain memorabilia of the local fishing history, but also to house a tribute to the late Kay Kendall, the actress. The lighthouse was opened in 1989 by Dr Rolla and her sister Kim Campbell as the Kay Kendall Memorial Museum. Born in Withernsea, Kay (a famous film star during the 1950s) and her family were very much involved with maritime life in the town. Her grandfather, Robert Drewery, worked on the construction of the lighthouse from 1891-1893, and he was also the coxswain on the last rowing off-shore lifeboat from 1911-1913. The base of the lighthouse displays many exhibits relating to the RNLI and HM Coastguard, including ships' bells, models, and old photographs recording the history of shipwrecks. There is also a special display that commemorates the Withernsea lifeboats and their crews, who saved 87 lives between 1862 and 1913. As the picture clearly shows, the lighthouse is now a prominent tourist attraction.

Withernsea, The Lighthouse 1955 W177010

Spurn Point Lighthouse

Navigation in the Humber estuary has always been a very difficult task, owing to the ever-shifting banks of sand around Spurn Point. Situated about 20 miles to the south of Hull, this area has a very interesting history. The earliest recorded light to be exhibited from Spurn Point was a small fire beacon positioned by a hermit's cottage during the 15th century. Even then, this light was never considered to be of much value because it was often moved about according to the direction of the wind.

With the return of the monarchy in 1660, the Lords of the Privy Council for Trade to Charles II were petitioned by numerous Hull ship owners for a light at Spurn Point. The project was strenuously opposed by Trinity House. However, the ship owners approached the owner of Spurn Point, Justinian Angell, and asked him to erect a lighthouse. They also agreed voluntarily to pay towards the upkeep of this coal-fired light. In 1672 Spurn Point exhibited its first purpose-built light, which proved to be a major success. Four years later, Justinian Angell applied for a Royal Patent which was approved; the terms stated that he could levy by compulsory means the sum of one farthing per ton from passing ships.

Originally there were two lights on this headland: the rear tower stood about 60ft high, and there was a low fire sited on a small platform arrangement. During the great storm of 1703, when hundreds of ships were lost along the whole of the east and south

Spurn Head, The Lighthouse 1899 44755

coasts, the wind fanned the Spurn Point fire to such an extent that the iron bars of the brazier melted. The keepers left the tower because they feared the structure would be burnt to the ground. The condition of the lights at Spurn Point in 1776 was extremely poor, so Trinity House forced the issue into the Court for the Lords of the Privy Council for Trade.

An Act of Parliament was passed which gave Trinity House the right to erect new lights; the cost was to be borne by the Angell family. This was successfully objected to by John Angell, and an agreement was reached that he should have the first option to build the new lighthouses.

Trinity House sent John Smeaton to Spurn Point in order to ensure that the new structures would be constructed to the proper specifications. When Smeaton informed Angell about the cost of the new lighthouses, it was far higher than he expected. In an attempt to reduce the expenditure, John Angell brought in a gang of 12 unruly labours from Spurn. He then kept them well supplied with beer and other liquor while they set about digging the foundations for the towers; during a drinking spree with the labourers Robert Foster, the keeper, mysteriously drowned. By the winter of 1777, the Smeaton-designed towers were in operation. The high light stood at 90ft high and the low tower at 50ft. Their enclosed coal fires required the employment of bellow blowers, who had to pump fresh air into the braziers all night.

Less than a year later, a terrific storm battered the Spurn headland, forcing the keepers and attendants to abandon the lighthouses. As the sea rose it crashed down around the towers; when a further huge wave rolled in, it washed the low light away. A few hours after this, a gigantic wave hit the high tower and smashed it to pieces. All the men could do was to watch this devastation unfolding in front of them. They also praised their keeper in charge, who had forced them to leave the lighthouses in plenty of time.

To overcome the loss, Trinity House insisted that the Angell family should erect some form of light as a temporary measure. A 'swape', which consisted of a long length of wood erected onto a timber frame like a sea-saw, weighted at one end and with a fire basket at the other, was provided, but there was very little that the Corporation could do at this time. Following the death of the childless John Angell in 1784, his estates at Spurn Point passed to Benedict John Angell Brown, who was a descendant of a female second cousin. This caused a great deal of friction in the Angell family, and the Corporation took full advantage of it. With Benedict appearing to be a lone figure, Trinity House assisted him in building a new lighthouse, yet the new 50ft tower was not completed until 1816.

In 1829 Spurn Point was once again battered by tremendous storms. This time they undermined the lighthouse; it was only saved by the quick action of the keepers, who propped up the structure using large boulders. After a long court action in 1839, Trinity House was able to purchase the Spurn Point light and take on the full responsibility of its upkeep. But on 28 December 1849 the sea tore through Spurn Point and carved a channel between the lighthouse and the mainland, which effectively left the tower standing on a small island. Further gales and storms occurred in March 1851, and this time the lighthouse was destroyed. However, the new lighting equipment that had been put into the lighthouse in 1848 was

salvaged. A temporary wooden structure was erected until a new low light was completed in June 1852. A new high lighthouse was built and erected 158 yards from the low tower, and the salvaged optical assembly and lighting equipment was installed. This stone tower had its light set at 50ft above the spring high water mark and was first lit on 29 November 1858.

A Trinity House Committee inspected the ruins of Smeaton's lighthouse in 1892 and discovered numerous cracks in the tower. Further examination revealed that the structure had settled because the wooden piles of the foundation had rotted. Smeaton's light had been built as near to the extreme point of the spit as possible; however, land erosion by the sea and a build up of silt had extended the point half a mile beyond its former position. Nevertheless, a site was chosen for a new lighthouse about 68 yards further back from the point. The new lighthouse was designed by Sir Thomas Matthews, the Engineer-in-Chief of Trinity House. Its foundations consisted of 21 hollow concrete cylinders, each 7ft in diameter and 22ft long. These were sunk vertically into an area 40ft in diameter and filled with concrete. More concrete was then poured between the cylinders to form the tower's base, making it a solid mass resting on the compacted shingle of the spit below. Upon this the 120ft-high lighthouse was built, using blue Staffordshire bricks. A barricade of stone encased in a timber framework was set up at the foot of the dunes in front of the lighthouse to protect it from erosion by the sea.

Instead of the former occulting light shown from Smeaton's tower, the new lantern at Spurn had a large 1st order dioptric lens assembly. This heavy unit stood in an annular tray filled with mercury. In turn it was rotated by a clockwork mechanism powered by a heavy weight which descended inside a hollow cast iron stanchion that was erected through the centre of the tower. Its light source was derived from a Douglass multi-wick oil burner. When lit, it produced a single flash every 20 seconds. Its recorded visible range for shipping was set at 17 nautical miles.

Three subsidiary lights were installed in the same tower. The first was a fixed white light, exhibited from a height of 60ft above high water to mark the Chequer Shoal. Another fixed red light was shown from the same height, but positioned to mark the Haile Sand Buoy. Both of these lights had a visible range of about 14 nautical miles. A further fixed white light was exhibited from a height of 45ft and directed up the Humber. This light had a visible range of around 12 nautical miles.

During the building programme, Smeaton's tower was propped up by baulks of timber until the Matthews lighthouse was completed. A short while later, the former tower was demolished and circular compound, and the curved cottages built against the perimeter wall were modernised. The new lighthouse also did away with the need for the low light. Its lantern was removed, and the tower was used by the Admiralty to store explosives. Later it was converted to a water tower. There were several modifications made to the lighting system installed in 1895. The first of

these was made during World War II. In 1941 it became necessary to make the light available for the use of allied convoys expected in the area, so the Spurn Point light was converted from oil to electricity. The electricity was supplied by the War Department, which had previously installed a diesel generator on the Point to supply the buildings used by the garrison.

Electricity continued in use until 1957, when it was replaced by acetylene gas lit on incandescent mantles. This highly inflammable gas was stored in high-pressure cylinders inside the lighthouse. The pressure of the stored gas also rotated the lantern. The 3 subsidiary lamps were changed to occulting operation, which means that they provided equal periods of light and dark every 30 seconds. The pressure of the stored gas also operated the occulting mechanism. The main light had its characteristic signal changed to flashes once every 15 seconds. On completion of this modernisation programme, Trinity House sent its keepers to other stations, because the operation of Spurn Point only needed six-monthly visits to change the gas cylinders. The Spurn Point light is now unmanned and automated.

Spurn Head, The Lighthouse 1899 44754

Hunstanton Lighthouse

Hunstanton, The Lighthouse 1891 28773

The area around Hunstanton is well known for its drifting sands and numerous underwater obstacles, which over hundreds of years have been treacherous for shipping. In August 1662 Charles II was presented with a petition for a navigational light at Hunstanton. It had been signed by the Mayor of Lynn, 183 ship owners, and worried mariners. It was clearly stated in this memorandum that they were prepared to pay a levy of '8d per chaldron of coal or 20 tons of other goods'. They also stipulated that the charge of 1d per ton be levied from all foreign vessels. When Trinity House was approached about the intended project, it was stated that its charter was for lights for shipping in general, and not for those which would be for local use. For this reason the Corporation would not erect a light at Hunstanton, but it had no objection if one was established by the local community.

A month later a Royal Letter Patent was awarded to John Knight, a court surgeon, who had previously assisted the King while exiled in France. When the Patent was first issued, many people expressed their concern that only one person's name had been put on the document. This was later clarified by the local Council. It stated that it had offered the Patent to John Knight because he was a very responsible and trustworthy person. The formal documents were issued in June 1665; at a cost of £200, two stone towers were built to show a clear channel through the treacherous sand banks.

In 1769, the philosopher and engineer Ezekiel Walker was commissioned to build a new lighthouse and to demolish the existing two lights. The main portion of his tower remains in place today.

When Trinity House purchased the Hunstanton light in 1838, it remained virtually unchanged for nearly 46 years; then in 1884 Trinity House carried out extensive repairs to the station, and built new dwellings for the keepers and their families. Prior to 1900, the Hunstanton lighthouse retained its drab granite colour. In 1902 Trinity House began its programme of painting its various towers with either red or black bands, for the purpose of making the lighthouses prominent day markers. Hunstanton received its red and white livery during the summer months of 1903. Hunstanton lighthouse was automated during the 1980s and was taken over by a consortium of Trustees.

A lifeboat was established at Hunstanton in 1867, with its boat house located to the north of the main town. There were 3 self-righting lifeboats, all named 'Licensed Victualler', which operated until the station was closed in 1931. In 1979 the Hunstanton station was re-opened and provided with a D-Class inshore lifeboat. In 1980 this vessel was replaced by an Atlantic 21 when Hunstanton was designated an all-year-round operational station. The original lifeboat house, built in 1867, was converted into a beach shop. This followed the construction of a new boathouse in 1900. This second boathouse remained in service until the station was closed in 1931, and was bought back by the RNLI when the station was reopened in 1979.

The present lifeboat is the 'B 749', and is an Atlantic 75-type inshore vessel. It was put on station on 10 September 1998 at the bequest of David Sissons, a member of the Haverhill RNLI Guild. The dedication ceremony was not carried out until a sunny yet somewhat breezy Sunday in May 1999. On this occasion she was formally named the 'D J S Haverhill' by Colin Spalding, on behalf of the donors and the Haverhill Branch of the RNLI. But even the best plans fail, and this official launch was no exception. When the lifeboat was towed out on her carriage by the tractor, the sea was extremely shallow. This required the tractor to push the carriage nearly 600 yards away from the beach, leaving the gathered guests wishing they had brought some binoculars to watch this demonstration launch. It was said that incidents like this clearly proved the need for a suitable pier at Hunstanton.

Hunstanton, The Lighthouse 1907 58899

Cromer Lighthouse

Originally the area on which the Cromer lighthouse stands was called Foulness. During the reign of Charles II, Sir John Clayton petitioned the King's Council for the erection of five towers on four sites. His proposal was for the Farne Islands off the coast of Northumberland, Flamborough Head in Yorkshire, Foulness at Cromer and two towers at Corton near Lowestoft.

For 39 years the Cromer lighthouse stood as a day mark. Then the increase in sea trade demanded a formal light. The new owner of the land at Cromer, Nathaniel Life, added a fire to the top of the existing Clayton tower. The Cromer lighthouse was officially lit on 29 September 1719. In 1781 Trinity House took over the ownership of the Cromer light. For a further 10 years it remained a coal-fired light; then in 1792 an Act of Parliament was passed which allowed the Corporation to erect a new lantern and to fit oil-burning Argand lamps and reflectors. It is recorded that the first keepers of the Cromer lighthouse in 1792 were both women, who between them received 'one pound each week with certain perquisites'.

Owing to serious land erosion, Trinity House commissioned James Walker to design and build a new lighthouse at Cromer in 1832. This octagonal tower was built to a height of 59ft with its light set at 276ft above sea level. Its location is about half a mile from the edge of the cliff. The Cromer lighthouse retained its oil-burning lamp until 1958, when the station was converted to electricity and in June 1990 the station was automated.

In 1805 the first lifeboat was established at Cromer. This Greathead-built North Country-type oars-only vessel was operated under the control of a local committee. The station was taken over by the Norfolk Shipwreck Association in 1823 and the RNLI took control in December 1857. At this time the station house was situated at the foot of the Gangway, which is a steep hill made of granite slabs, with their corners sticking up as a means to provide a grip for horses' hooves as they pulled cargo carriages up from the beach. In 1902 a larger lifeboat house was built on the same site.

The Cromer pier was built in 1900 with a slipway of 165ft. Later a new lifeboat house was constructed at its end for the first motor lifeboat to be stationed at Cromer. When this lifeboat arrived in 1923, the old vessel was retained; this was because at certain states of the weather it was impossible to re-house the motorised boat at the end of the pier. In 1967 an inshore lifeboat was sent to the station, and an ILB house was built in 1984 on the Promenade to the east of the Gangway. The boat house built in 1902 is now the Cromer Lifeboat Museum, with the former lifeboat 'H F Bailey' on display inside. Overlooking the boathouse, outside the Old Watch House, is a bust of former Coxswain Henry Blogg. In 1997 the house at the end of the pier was demolished and replaced by a larger house. The new house and slipway were constructed in 1998; they became operational on 4 March 1999, which coincided with the 175th Anniversary of the RNLI.

Cromer, The Lighthouse 1894 33326

Lowestoft Lighthouse

Lowestoft, The Lighthouse 1921 71705

Prior to 1608, Trinity House resisted all petitions by shipowners and merchants to provide a lighthouse at Lowestoft. However the tragic loss of life, ships and valuable cargoes came to the attention of the Privy Council of James I, who forced the Corporation to reconsider. Trinity House applied for a Letter Patent in November 1608; by April 1609, the Corporation had two lighthouses built 'for the direction of ships which crept by night in the dangerous passage betwixt Lowestoft and Winterton'. The Lowestoft high tower was a formidable 80ft-high timber structure that stood on the cliff top overlooking the harbour. On the ness, 100ft below the cliff, another 65ft-high tower was erected. Both of these lighthouses were topped by glazed lanterns; the light came from a chandelier of tallow candles.

In May 1621, Trinity House sent William Cooke, a mariner from Wapping, and Sir Michael Geere to carry out the urgent repairs to the Lowestoft lighthouses. Thanks to the extent of the damage, a new high tower was erected in the summer of 1628 approximately 225ft further back from the cliff face. For 46 years the Lowestoft lights remained in service, with numerous repairs being carried out, but the instability of the low lighthouse was noticeable in high winds, and it needed strengthening several times.

In 1675, Trinity House demolished the existing Lowestoft high light and replaced it with a stone tower. This lighthouse had an open coal fire brazier. Above the doorway to the tower, a marble plaque was positioned with an inscription and Trinity House's coat of arms. Lowestoft was the first lighthouse to have a marble plaque; this started the customary practice for all the Corporation's lighthouses. Within months of Trinity House's completing the Lowestoft lighthouse, the open fire sent dangerous sparks and embers into the air and threatened to set fire to the town, which was only 240ft from the lighthouse. The fire was then enclosed in a lantern, however, the lantern caused such a dramatic loss of illumination, that Trinity House employed a gang of blowers to pump air into the fire with heavy leather bellows.

The Lowestoft low light remained a serious problem, for the sea continued to undermine its foundations. Following a very severe south-westerly storm in February 1831, the keepers reported that they believed the tower was about to collapse. A second storm three weeks later broke the glass in the coal fired lantern. The sudden blast of air set fire to the tower and turned it into a raging inferno. In May 1831, Trinity House sent their Consultant Engineer Daniel Asher Alexander to survey the damaged Lowestoft low light. On his return to London he designed a new tower, and gave the project to his trainee engineer Richard Suter. Over the next twelve months, Richard Suter supervised the building of the new low light and carried out the construction of the Pakefield lighthouse further along the coast.

In 1874 the present-day lighthouse was constructed. It stands nearly 53ft high, with its light set at about 122ft above sea level and it provided a visible range of 28 nautical miles. The Lowestoft lighthouse was eventually electrified in July 1936. During May 1975, Trinity House completed the automation programme for the Lowestoft lighthouse and the keepers left the station for the last time.

A lifeboat was first established at Lowestoft in 1802; it is one of the oldest stations in the area. In 1807 Lionel Lukin designed and built the 'Frances Ann' lifeboat, which was provided by the Suffolk Humane Society. The RNLI took over the Lowestoft lifeboat in March 1855 and established a No 2 station in 1870. From 1882 the large No 1 lifeboat was put on moorings in the harbour and this has remained the method of launching ever since. In 1921 the first motor lifeboat was sent to the station. In 1998 a new facility and a workshop was built on the site of the former Pier Pavilion and new pontoon mooring in the south-eastern corner of the Yacht Basin was provided as part of the development of the marina. This lifeboat facility was formally opened at a ceremony held on 16 July 1999.

Southwold Lighthouse

The ancient borough of Southwold was granted a charter by Henry VII in 1489 which gave it the status of a Town Corporate with all its privileges. In May 1672 a sea battle was fought between the British and the combined French and Dutch fleets. James, Duke of York, brother of Charles II, was Lord High Admiral of England at this time, and had his headquarters in an early Elizabethan house in the High Street.

The chief glory of Southwold must be its magnificent church (1460) dedicated to St Edmund, Christian martyr and the last King of East Anglia. Its tower, some 100ft high, with characteristic flint decorations, watches benignly over the town. One of the town's most attractive features is its common, which extends into the Town Marshes and down to the River Blyth. The Blyth, once a busy commercial waterway, today plays host to a picturesque flotilla of yachts, pleasure craft and long shore fishing boats.

The Southwold lighthouse was established as a coastal marker for passing ships and as a guide for vessels entering the local harbour. In order to ensure that the light was easily recognised, it was built near the centre of this seaside resort. Its position is set at the midway point between Lowestoft and Orford.

Construction of the Southwold lighthouse, designed by Sir James Nicholas Douglass, began in 1887. A temporary light on a wooden tower first showed an illumination on the 19 February 1889 and on 3 September 1893, three years after this photograph was taken, the Southwold light was first lit. This tower is 102ft in height with its light set at 121ft above sea level, with a visible distance between 15 and 18 nautical miles. Originally the light source was provided by a multi-wick oil burner but in 1906 this was replaced by an incandescent oil burner similar to a large gas mantle arrangement. In 1938 the Southwold light was electrified and automated by means of numerous time clocks and the keepers left the lighthouse and were sent to other stations. Today an attendant keeper regularly visits the lighthouse. Part of the tower is being used as a museum and the lighthouse is listed as an architectural and historical building of great interest.

In 1893 the Southwold lifeboat service was established by the RNLI. Its first vessel was the 44ft-long 'Alfred Corry', which was built by Beeching Brothers of Great Yarmouth at a cost of £490 7s 6d. The money was provided by the RNLI, who used money left to them by Kensington-born A J Corry who had died at the age of 34. Although there is no record to state how he died at such a young age, it is known that he bequeathed the funds to the RNLI as a means of thanking the Cork lifeboat, which had saved his

Southwold, The Lighthouse and East Green 1893
32184

Southwold, The Lighthouse 1891 28354

mother and father. It is also known that A J Corry had no connection with the sea. The 'Alfred Corry' was a Norfolk & Suffolk-type, non-self-righting, sailing and rowing lifeboat. She had 2 masts and needed a crew of 18 oarsmen. Without the crew she weighed 8.3 tons. After 1908, she was moved into the newly-refurbished harbour and launched from a specially built platform or slipway.

During her years of active service, the 'Alfred Corry' was launched on 41 occasions and saved 47 lives. Her first coxswain was John Cragie (1893-1898), who was followed by Sam May (1898-1918). Her last months of operational duty were from October to December 1918 with her coxswain Charles Jarvis. Many well-known families in Southwold have crewed the 'Alfred Corry', and these include such names as Palmer, Hurr, Goldsmith, Waters, Upcraft, Ladd, Peck, Stannard, Herrington, Rogers, Took, Barber, Crickmore and Chapman.

After the Great War she was found to be in need of considerable repair, and was condemned and sold out of service to Lord Albemarle, who converted her to a fine yacht named the 'Alba'. In 1949 she was renamed the 'Thorfinn', but by 1976 it appeared that no-one was concerned about this historic vessel. After ending up as a derelict houseboat at Maldon in Essex, she was bought by Captain John Cragie (great-grandson of her first coxswain) and his wife Doreen after a long search. By 1979 they had restored her back to a yacht; this time she was re-launched with her original name, 'Alfred Corry'. By 1991 she was again in need of repairs. Although they wanted to keep her as a yacht, John and Doreen decided to bring her back to Southwold and started a Trust to save her. The first thing that they did was to strip off the finery and then restore her to the original lifeboat form. Today the 'Alfred Corry' is preserved to ensure she survives as a memorial to all of the crews who served on her.

Languard Lighthouse

Harwich, Landguard Lighthouse 1906 54659

The historic maritime naval port of Harwich lies at the mouth of the River Orwell in Essex. Today it has become an important ferry terminal for ships sailing to the Hook of Holland. The entrance to the harbour is dominated by two forts, the Redoubt and the Landguard. In 1340 Harwich was the departure point for the massive fleet of Edward III when it set sail on a mission to destroy the French at the Battle of Sluys.

The history of the lighthouses established at Harwich revolves around Sir William Batten. Samuel Pepys clearly acknowledged this knight of the realm in his diaries. He stated: 'as a gentleman he is a great man at the taverns'. Sir William Batten was an Admiral in the English Navy, and later became the Master of Trinity House. During the summer of 1664, Sir William requested the assistance of Samuel Pepys with an application for a Royal Patent to erect two lighthouses near the entrance to Harwich dockyard.

Sir William Batten was issued with his Royal Patent in 1665 for a period of 61 years at a £5 annual rent to the Crown. He was authorised to obtain by compulsory means the sum of one farthing from English ships and a half penny from foreign vessels for the upkeep of the lights.

As the war with the Dutch escalated during 1666, the Navy Board seriously considered blowing up the Harwich lights and erecting a canvas painting of a lighthouse further along the coast to the east. The reasoning behind this idea was that the Dutch would be confused into believing it was the Harwich light and sail onto the treacherous rock nearby. To prevent this action by the Navy Board, Sir William Batten posted a heavy guard around his lighthouses, with explicit orders to kill anyone who tried to carry out this ridiculous idea. Two years after the Harwich lights came into operation, Sir William Batten died. In

October 1667 the Patent for the lights passed to his wife; but when the will of Sir William was read, he left the responsibility for managing the Harwich lights to his Negro servant Mingo. A clause stated that 'the custody and keeping of my two lights, along with the sum of £20, be given to Mingo for his long and faithful service'.

In 1815, Trinity House took over the full management of the lights. A year later Daniel Asher Alexander, the Corporation's consultant architect, began the erection of one 9-sided and a companion 10-sided structure. In 1836 Trinity House purchased the Harwich Lights from General Rebow, the last lessee, for £31,730; the amount was based upon the loss of revenue he would have received from the remaining 12 years and 5 days of his lease. It is also believed that the shrewd General Rebow was clearly aware of the rapid changes in the course of the channel. Had the lease continued, he would have been liable for building new towers at different locations. The lighthouses became redundant in 1863 for just this reason, and the new cast iron structures were erected at Dovercourt near the present Phoenix Hotel. The high lighthouse continued to be used by mariners as a seamark. These high and low towers were about 40ft and 24ft in height respectively. These lights remained in service until 1863, when two new towers were built.

In 1909, the low lighthouse was sold to the Borough Council. It was vested with the Harwich Corporation for 10s (50p), but with the condition that it should be returned to Trinity House if it was needed for navigational purposes. In 1970 Trinity House converted the lighthouse into a pilot signal station. In 1974, it reverted to the District Council on completion of the new Pilot Station at Angel Gate. It became the Maritime Museum of the Harwich Society in 1980.

As the picture shows, in 1906 the Landguard tower had its own separate dwelling for the keepers. This particular station was not considered to be one of the main lights; it was established in 1845. Its position was set so that it showed a red light from the Beach End buoy and a white light visible to the west. The Harwich lighthouses built in 1863 were of a cast iron pile construction. Each of them consisted of an octagonal cast iron hut on top of a trellis of iron piles.

The Harwich lights were discontinued in 1964 when new pier lights were established, but they remained as tourist attractions for many years. Dovercourt in Harwich is better known today as the Trinity House control centre, which monitors all the automated lights around England and Wales.

Harwich, Landguard Lighthouse Keepers on Duty 1906 54659A

North Foreland Lighthouse

The North Foreland Lighthouse 1908 60383

The North Foreland light at Broadstairs on the North Kent coast is an important navigational aid which warns shipping of the treacherous Goodwin Sands. However, in 1634 Trinity House strongly opposed the construction of a lighthouse; the Corporation stated that a light in this location would assist the King's enemies at a time of war. Despite this opposition, the petition from Sir John Meldrum for the South and North Foreland lights was backed by numerous concerned ship owners and masters. With this substantial backing, Charles I personally ordered his Privy Council to issue a Royal Letter Patent for the project. The two sites would be 15 miles apart, and would come under the ownership of Sir John Meldrum for a period of 50 years at a £20 annual rent to the Crown Treasury.

Sir John Meldrum built two lighthouses; they were made of oak, covered with softwood laths and coated with sand-based rendering. Each tower had an open coal-burning brazier, which were first lit in August 1635. During the first three years, adverse weather conditions and high winds caused the lighthouses to be destroyed by fire. On several occasions the wind toppled the structures, which meant that Sir John Meldrum had to build new ones.

Another successful lighthouse project was already under way at Winterton and Wintertoness, where the Patent was owned by Sir William Erskine. Sir John Meldrum invited Sir William to join him in his Foreland project, mainly to offset the high cost of maintaining the lights. There was no objection from Trinity House about the renewal of the Foreland Patent, because of a clever agreement reached by Erskine and Meldrum with the Corporation. This deal was orchestrated by Samuel Pepys, which stated that at the end of the 35-year Patent, it would pass over to the Greenwich Hospital Trustees as part of the partners' wills.

On one occasion during the winter months of 1690, the keepers were forced to leave the North Foreland lighthouse in order to evade the press gangs. This effectively caused the light to be extinguished.

The local Church of England minister found the frightened men and persuaded them to return with him to the lighthouse. As soon as the light was re-lit, the press gang returned, but fearing the wrath of God they refused to remove the vicar from the base of the tower.

The treacherous Goodwin Sands stretch all the way from South Foreland and around to the North Foreland lighthouse. In 1703 this area became the scene of one of the greatest disasters in British shipping history. On 19th November severe hurricane-force winds and tremendous storms began to batter the southern coastline of England. By 23 November the weather had calmed down, but numerous buildings had been destroyed and hundreds of ships had been wrecked or blown ashore along the coast. Many people believed the tremendous storm was over, but in fact they were now in the eye of a major hurricane. When the hurricane finally subsided, the devastation was unbelievable. The coastline was a mass of wreckage and bodies. The entrances to the harbours were completely blocked with ships floating upside down. Out of the 160 ships known to have anchored around the Goodwin Sands, only 70 were salvageable, and just 10 were in reasonable condition. A total of 1,334 mariners had been drowned. By the summer of 1704 the North Foreland lighthouse had been rebuilt.

In 1719 the Patent for the Foreland lights was bequeathed to the Trustees of Greenwich Hospital. During the early part of 1792, the Trustees obtained the services of architect John Yenn; he was to demolish the existing tower and build a new masonry lighthouse. This hexagonal tower was built at Broadstairs to a height of 85ft and with its light standing 188ft above the highest spring water tide level. On completion of this work, the previous keeper from the old light, Henry Knott, took on the post of Keeper-in-Charge. This keeper would now put his name into the lighthouse history books as being the man who began the longest-serving family of keepers at a single station. He started this job in 1730, and the family continued to pass the job from father to son for 180 years until 1911

In 1836 the North Foreland lighthouse was purchased by Trinity House. From that time the Corporation took over the full management of the station and employed its own keepers. Over the following 162 years, routine repairs and the modernisation of its equipment and lighting systems were carried out. However, the station has remained very much as it was when first built by John Yenn. The Duke of Edinburgh in his capacity of Master of Trinity House officiated at the handing-over ceremony of the lighthouse following its automation in November 1998. When the keepers left North Foreland, they were the last of the traditional on-station keepers to be employed by Trinity House. This also made North Foreland the last light to be automated around the British Isles.

The North Foreland Lighthouse 1894 34192

Ramsgate Lighthouse

Ramsgate harbour was originally built as a port of refuge for vessels sheltering from stormy weather. In 1821 George IV visited Ramsgate; because of the enthusiastic welcome he received, the King proclaimed that the harbour would be conferred with a unique Royal title.

This harbour has played a very important role throughout its history. It became one of the prime embarkation ports during the Napoleonic war, which is why the main highway in the town is called Military Road. In 1940, thousands of soldiers arrived at Ramsgate harbour in hundreds of small boats, following their dramatic evacuation from the French beaches of Dunkirk. Today some of these vessels are moored in the Ramsgate marina. One of these small boats, the 'Sundowner' owned by Mr Lightoller, took his son Roger and 17-year-old Sea Scout Gerry Ashcroft to Dunkirk. He felt that if anyone was going to sail his boat, then it should be he, and not some inexperienced naval rating who had no knowledge of the craft. The contribution that the 58ft 'Sundowner' made during the amazing evacuation of 338,000 men was to rescue 130 soldiers in one trip. As time passed,

she was threatened with destruction owing to her very dilapidated condition, but in 1986 the Marina Trust carried out a major restoration project, which has seen the 'Sundowner' returning to a new life at sea. During this war-time period, Ramsgate was also a base for the Royal Navy torpedo boats.

Yet back in 1750, Ramsgate harbour did not contain yachts and fast passenger-carrying catamarans, but a large fleet of fishing trawlers and small ships. Most of these coastal vessels were employed in transporting goods between Kent and various ports around the British Isles. By 1815 the volume of sea trade using Ramsgate harbour was colossal; this meant that better facilities were needed, such as breakwaters and piers. Over the next few years the Harbour Board instigated major changes and erected proper navigational lights around the port. This involved the building of 4 lights around the harbour, two of which were built on the cliffs on either side of the port. Both of these showed a green light to guide shipping through the Old Cudd Channel. On the east pier a stone tower was erected; its beam continually flashed a white light every 5 seconds throughout the night. On the west pier stood the lighthouse shown in the picture, which had a special lighting arrangement. By means of a large steel float directly under the tower and protected by the pier, the light would change from red to green. If the water level was below 10ft, a green screen covered the light. If the water was above 10ft, a red screen was lifted as the water level rose. Today these lights are still in service.

Ramsgate, The Pier Lighthouse 1901 48035

South Foreland Lighthouse

Between the North and South Foreland lighthouse is one of the most dangerous stretches of water in the British Isles: this covers the notorious Goodwin Sands. This mariners' nightmare has claimed an unbelievable number of lives and ships throughout its history. There are two main townships nearby, Ramsgate and Deal. The worst recorded historical facts about this region are the stories of the heartless people who literally ignored the drowning mariners in preference to salvaging the cargoes from their wrecked ships.

When the Romans arrived in Britain, there was a waterway between Thanet and the mainland, which they used to avoid rounding the dangerous North Foreland. This strip of waterway was known as the Wantsum Channel. The channel was wide enough for a safe haven and here ships and galleys could shelter from the worst of the weather. As further protection, the Romans established the garrisons of Reculver and Richborough at each end of the waterway. However, throughout the centuries of Roman occupation the Wantsum Channel slowly silted up and became a narrow stretch of water. While these changes were taking place, the shingle bank of the Goodwin Sands was slowly growing towards the north.

When relative peace came during the rule of the Normans and Plantagenets, considerable trade developed between Britain and Europe. The area near the Goodwin Sands became known as the Downs and the shingle bank had effectively silted up the Stour estuary; by the middle of the 15th century, the Downs had become an important anchorage. Sailing ships that needed to round the North Foreland in both directions had to wait for favourable winds before they could continue their voyage and for this reason the Downs provided a great deal of protection against wind and weather. However, timing was important for any ship attempting a voyage around North Foreland and towards London. Any error of judgement would see this vessel driven ashore by the strong currents, where in nearly every case it became a total loss.

The South Foreland Lighthouse 1898 40814

During this period, the number of ships anchored up might be several hundred. The weather often caused some of them to break away from their mooring and to be helplessly driven aground along the Goodwin Sands. Local boatmen and offshore men living in makeshift shacks along the shingle bank eagerly took advantage of this. The peculiarities and dangers of the stretch of water between Deal and the Goodwin Sands brought about a special breed of very skilled seamen. Their thorough experience of sailing near the Downs made them the ideal men for the King's vessels and merchant ships. It was these men that the Corporation of Trinity House first employed as its pilots following the issuing of its Charter by Henry VIII.

With the majority of the Downs men well-versed in the heartless wrecking, their employment seemed to be the best way to break this cruel custom. Most of the men later obtained full master's tickets; when they returned home from a life at sea, they served as pilots through these dangerous waters. One of the main incentives for the men during the 17th century was the issuing of special exemption certificates which protected them from the vicious press gangs.

South Foreland is situated above St Margaret's Bay in Kent, and is 15 miles from its companion light of North Foreland. It is also just 4 miles to the north-east of Dover. This former operational lighthouse previously warned shipping about the treacherous Goodwin Sands. As we saw in the North Foreland story, South Foreland was established in 1635 and was built by Sir John Meldrum. In 1792 the architect John Yenn designed and built the present lighthouse, and also constructed a similar tower at North Foreland. At this time the lighthouse station was owned by the Trustees of the Greenwich Hospital. George Knott was the third in a succession of five generations of a family of lighthouse keepers who are accredited with the longest period of continuous service in history. He

joined the lighthouse service as a keeper at South Foreland in 1730. George was famous for his wonderful models of the lighthouses in which he served along with his brother William Knott. This family tradition ended with Henry T Knott at North Foreland in 1911.

The South Foreland Lighthouse 1900 44901

Following the discovery of electricity by Michael Faraday in 1831, Frederick Holmes devised a method for generating this 'mysterious power'. When its discovery reached the scientific community, it was considered to be a simple device. In its basic form, magnetism is the key to electricity. If a permanent bar magnet is moved backwards and forwards inside a coil of insulated copper wire, electricity will be produced. Frederick Holmes took this principle a step further and devised a massive magneto electric generator. Mounted on a large wooden frame, this 2-ton assembly contained a circle of 36 magnets, each weighing about 50 pounds. This wheel-like construction was revolved at 600rpm to pass a set of copper bars, and electric current was produced.

Trials were first carried out at the Trinity House experimental station at Blackwall, London, in 1857. Then, on 8 December 1858, South Foreland became the first lighthouse in the British Isles to be illuminated by electricity. The system was nothing like we would expect today. To produce the electricity, two massive coal- or coke-burning steam engines were required to drive the 2-ton generator. Once this direct current was produced, it energised a pair of carbon arc rods which formed an extremely bright illumination. Numerous problems arose during the first few months. The main difficulty was the insulated copper wires carrying the electricity, which nearly set fire to the lighthouse; these cables were closely clipped to the walls and floors, and the induced current over-heated them. The rubber insulation bubbled, then produced a horrible fuming gas. When the keepers identified the problem, they shut down the machinery and installed a Douglass multi-wick oil burner. Over the subsequent months all the cables were suspended in metal loops to allow a proper circulation of air around the wires.

The problem was not overcome until the introduction of alternating current in 1867, when Frederick Holmes perfected a dynamo electric generator without a commutator. This advance in technology was first shown by Trinity House at the Paris Exhibition of 1868, when an electric light was lit on top of a 120ft-high scaffold. By 1869 Trinity House had adopted the new Holmes dynamo electric generator, and installed one at South Foreland. This time another problem arose: the actual dynamo over-heated. An experiment with a large fan placed behind the assembly and driven by the belts of the steam engines proved very satisfactory.

Over the next few years keepers from other land-based stations such as Souter Point, Dungeness and Lizard Point were sent to South Foreland to be trained in the use of electricity. South Foreland has been a testing station for numerous inventions; Marconi used it for his first radio message sent across the Channel, for example. Much of the former equipment used by Marconi at South Foreland can be seen in the Science Museum in London. This lighthouse is no longer in use; now administered by the National Trust, in 1988 the South Foreland lighthouse became one of the most visited stations

The South Foreland Lighthouse 1924 76104

around the British Isles.

As the years passed, 3 lifeboat stations were established, one each at Kingsdown, Walmer and North Deal. They took on the rescue work that had formerly been carried out by the Deal luggers. Their exploits are well recorded by the Rev Treanor in his book 'Heroes of the Goodwin Sands'.

However, one significant introduction in 1802 was the establishment of the first lifeboat, which was built by Greathead for the Trustees of Ramsgate Harbour. This station did not appear to be very effective until just before 1824, when the Harbour Trustees purchased a lifeboat built by Beeching of Great Yarmouth. Later, the RNLI jointly controlled the station from 1865 until 1922 along with the Board of Trade. It then took over the full management of the Ramsgate lifeboat.

The list of bravery awards which have been presented to the Ramsgate lifeboat station shows an extremely impressive record. 1829: Silver medal awarded to Captain Edward Gimar for the rescue of the crew of six from the French brigantine 'Auguste' in December 1828. 1857: Silver medal awarded to Coxswain J Hogbin for assisting with the rescue of 18 people from the brigantine 'Caminha', which was wrecked during gale force winds on the Goodwin Sands on 26 November. 1864: Silver medal awarded to Coxswain I Jarman for his assistance in saving a large number of shipwrecked people during the heavy gales of December 1863, particularly in rescuing 120 lives from the emigrant ship 'Fusilier' on 3 December 1863.

A tragic event occurred in 1873: a member of the Ramsgate lifeboat crew William White, was washed overboard and lost while assisting the Norwegian barge 'Sarpsborg' on 2 February. 1881: Gold medal awarded to Coxswain C Fish after the lifeboat under his command rescued 12 of the 29 crewmen from the barque 'Indian Chief'. She was wrecked on the Long Sand in an easterly gale and heavy sea on 5 January, while on passage to Yokohama from Middlesborough. Silver medals were awarded to 11 other members of the lifeboat crew and to 7 crew members of the tug 'Vulcan' which towed the lifeboat. The last surviving member of this lifeboat crew died in May 1931.

1892: Silver medal and £1 each awarded to James Watson, William Burton, Edwin Hurle and Arthur E Fisher, the crew of the smack 'Britain's Pride' of Ramsgate, for saving an apprentice from the ship 'Enterkin' of Glasgow, which was wrecked on the Galloper Sands in a heavy westerly gale on 12 December 1891. 1906: Silver medal awarded to John Hawkins for his bravery in lowering himself by a rope from the East Pier and swimming out to the assistance of 5 people whose boat had capsized off the harbour entrance in a strong west-south-westerly wind and

rough sea on 14 September. All five were saved. 1916: Silver medal awarded to Coxswain W Cooper and Second Coxswain T W Read for rescuing the crew of 52 from the SS 'Siberia', wrecked on the Goodwin Sands on 20 November. The lifeboat was constantly full of water, and nearly capsized on several occasions. The crew of the vessel were eventually taken off by the Kingsdown lifeboat.

On 24 August 1940, the Ramsgate station had to be closed. The town was bombed during that day, and the lifeboat crew of 9 took shelter in a cellar near the harbour. A bomb exploded outside, and 6 of the men were wounded. Up to 1940, the Ramsgate station had already rescued 168 lives since the outbreak of the war. The station was re-opened on 11 October 1940, although the coxswain, assistant motor mechanic and one of the crew were still unfit for duty.

The outstanding service of the Ramsgate station during the war was its work on the beaches of Dunkirk. The lifeboat 'Prudential' evacuated 2,800 men of the British Expeditionary Force. When she got

The South Foreland Lighthouse 1924 76105

back to Ramsgate, she had been away for over 40 hours. For 30 hours she had been close to the beaches, and throughout this period she was constantly under fire. Her crew continued with this important rescue for 2 nights without sleep. Her coxswain, Howard Primrose Knight, was awarded the Distinguished Service Medal for his 'gallantry and determination in this work'. As well as helping at Dunkirk, the Ramsgate lifeboat was launched 60 times and rescued 170 lives between 1939 and 1945.

1952: Bronze medal awarded to Coxswain Douglas S Kirkaldie for the rescue of five men from the fore part of the SS 'Western Farmer' of New York on 20/21 August. The 'Western Farmer' had broken in two, and Coxswain Kirkaldie brought the lifeboat alongside the stern section, although it was clear that it might turn over on top of the lifeboat. This Coxswain also received the Maud Smith Award for the bravest act of life-saving in 1952. 1968: The inscribed vellum awarded to Coxswain Thomas J H Cooper for saving the yacht 'Lungta' and rescuing her crew of four after the yacht had grounded on Ramsgate harbour bar in a strong south-westerly gale and a very rough sea during the night of 11/12 October.

1975: The inscribed vellum awarded to crew members Michael Petts and Timothy Hurst for entering the sea to escort to the lifeboat 3 men and one woman from the yacht 'Albas' grounded on the Goodwin Sands in a strong south-south-westerly wind and a rough sea during the night of 11/12 September 1980: The inscribed vellum awarded to Malcolm H R Llewellyn and Bryan L E Morgan, Coxswain and Launch Seaman respectively of the Trinity House Pilot Vessel 'Versatile', in recognition of their skill and determination when the pilot vessel rescued an angler washed off the East Pier, Ramsgate, in a northerly storm and a rough steep sea on 29 November.

1983: A framed letter signed by the RNLI Chairman, the Duke of Atholl, awarded to Coxswain/Mechanic R Cannon and his crew, 2nd Coxswain/Assistant Mechanic D Pegden, Emergency Mechanic D Cooper, Crew Members W Blay, T Brown and T Hurst, in recognition of the rescue of the crew of 6 from the yacht 'Mer Gaspard' on 30 October. This

yacht had gone aground at the eastern edge of the Goodwin Knoll Bank and was lying on to her starboard side being battered by heavy seas. Even so, the lifeboat crew managed to take the yacht in tow to Ramsgate. 1984: A framed letter signed by the RNLI Chairman, the Duke of Atholl, awarded to the Coxswain/Mechanic R Cannon, 2nd Coxswain/Assistant Mechanic D Pegden, Crew Members T Hurst, M Mett, N Stephens and R Noble in recognition of their skill when the lifeboat rescued the crew of 2 from the trawler 'Nancy' after she fouled her propeller about 2 miles from North Foreland on 30 January. The lifeboat also managed to tow the trawler into Ramsgate Harbour.

1985: The inscribed vellum awarded to Helmsman Timothy E Hurst for saving the cabin cruiser 'Hide and Seek' and rescuing her crew of 2 after the boat had suffered engine failure and was being pounded against the western breakwater during a southerly storm on 11 August. 1986: Silver medal awarded to Coxswain/Mechanic Ronald N Cannon in recognition of the courage displayed by him when the French fishing vessel 'Gloire a Marie II' ran aground at the entrance to the River Stour 2 miles south-west of Ramsgate. She was towed into deep water along with her 7 crew and led to safety during a north-easterly hurricane with 20ft-high seas breaking over them on 26 December 1985.

2000: Silver Second Service Clasp awarded to Coxswain/Mechanic Ronald N Cannon in recognition of the enormous courage demonstrated by him when the yacht 'Rasmus' and her crew of 3 were saved from the Goodwin Sands in atrocious weather conditions on 9 November 1999. Emergency Mechanic Timothy Hurst and crew member Lance Oran were each accorded the inscribed vellum for their part in this service, which involved both the all-weather and the inshore lifeboats. Coxswain/Mechanic Ronald Cannon also received the Miss Maud Smith Reward for Courage in memory of John, 7th Earl of Hardwicke.

Dungeness

In the summer of 1599, Sir Edward Hayward informed Elizabeth I about the numerous ship owners who were requesting a navigational light on his land at Dungeness. Trinity House was approached about the petition for Dungeness, but in 1600 the Corporation insisted that a lighthouse was unnecessary and declined to build one. When James I ascended to the throne of England, another petition was presented for the establishment of a light at Dungeness. This application was handed to the King in 1615; it was signed by hundreds of ship owners, many of whose home ports were many miles from Dungeness. A Royal Letter Patent was given to Sir Edward Hayward to erect a light for 50 years at an annual rent to the Crown of £5. He was also authorised to collect a levy at one farthing per ton from passing ships for the upkeep of the light, but he was not allowed to demand any dues from the King's ships. Sir Edward then erected a 5ft high coal-burning iron brazier on top of a small rubble stone tower positioned near the edge of the headland.

**Dungeness, The Old Lighthouse
c1965** D165013

Displaying a light was one thing, but forcing ship owners to pay for its upkeep proved to be very difficult. Those ship owners who had promised to contribute towards the Dungeness light now did everything they could to avoid the agents sent out by Sir Edward Hayward. By 1620, this situation had brought Sir Edward close to bankruptcy. He explained his concerns to the Clerk of the Royal Kitchens, William Lamplough, who decided to purchase the rights of the Patent and pay a £5 annual rent for the land on which the light had been erected.

William Lamplough investigated the problems in collecting the light dues. After a meeting with local customs officers, an agreement was reached whereby a commission of 20% would be paid for their services in enforcing the levy. Meanwhile, Trinity House still maintained the belief that a light at Dungeness was unnecessary and a financial burden on shipping. Ship owners who had previously supported the establishing of the light now joined sides with the Corporation to have it discontinued. When the Corporation promoted a Bill in Parliament in 1630, the ship owners supported its claim that the light was barely visible. (William Lamplough had demolished the coal-fired light and erected a candle-burning lantern on top of a tall pole). Fearing that he would be forced to compensate William Lamplough if he revoked his Patent, Charles I instructed his Parliament to reject the Bill. However, he ordered William Lamplough to build a prominent light, or else his Patent would be cancelled.

By 1635, William Lamplough had built a new tower and a keeper's cottage on the Dungeness headland. This structure is believed to been about 20ft in height, and topped with a large coal-burning brazier. For a further 20 years this light continued in service, and began to make a handsome profit for William

Dungeness, The Old Lighthouse c1965 D165017

the English Channel. It was also one of the more profitable privately-owned lights around the British Isles. After a disastrous winter when the lighthouse was burnt to the ground, John Lamplough surrendered his Patent to Trinity House one year before it expired. Yet before Trinity House took on the Dungeness light, they ordered John Lamplough to build a new tower; after many arguments with the Corporation's surveyors, it was completed by the end of 1719.

In 1789, Trinity House decided to establish a new lighthouse along with better keepers' quarters. Samuel Wyatt, the Corporation's consultant architect, was commissioned to design and build the new tower and outbuildings closer to the headland. By September 1791 this project was completed. The tower stood at 92ft above sea level, and inside its large lantern was an assembly of oil-burning Argand lamps and catoptric reflectors. The beam produced was visible on a clear night for 15 nautical miles.

In August 1861, the Dungeness lighthouse was struck by lightning and one of the keepers seriously hurt. While repairs were being carried out by Lewis William Wyatt, the son of its previous builder, a temporary oil-burning lamp inside a lantern was erected on top of a wooden tower. The repairs took

Lamplough. However, in 1655 the Parliament of Oliver Cromwell withdrew his Patent under the new rules of the Commonwealth. Following the return of the monarchy, William Lamplough was given back his Dungeness Patent in 1661; it was extended by a further 5 years until 1670, in order to compensate him for the loss of income during the short-lived Commonwealth.

In 1670 William Lamplough applied for his Patent to be renewed. With the light now proving to be in good order, Trinity House offered no objection to this application. By December of the same year, a new Patent had been issued for a period of 50 years. A year later William Lamplough died, and in his will he bequeathed the Patent to his son John. During the term of the second Patent the Dungeness light proved to be one of the most important navigational aids along

**Dungeness, The Old Lighthouse
The Keepers' Quarters c1965** D165013A

until June 1862 and the oil lamps were replaced by new electric lights. This followed the successful trials of electricity that had been under way at the South Foreland lighthouse since December 1858.

Samuel Wyatt's tower continued in service until 1940, when German fighter pilots used the undefended lighthouse for target practice. After the war, Sir John Bowen was given the task of supervising the repairs. The Dungeness lighthouse provided a further 15 years of faithful service until a nuclear power station was built nearby. This effectively prevented the light from being seen by shipping that passed on voyages down the English Channel. Today the former Samuel Wyatt lighthouse of 1791 still stands close to its unusual circular dwelling. It is privately owned, but it has been restored so that visitors can tour this historic lighthouse.

In 1960, Philip Hunt, the Engineer-in-Chief for Trinity House, became responsible for the building of a new lighthouse tower at Dungeness. This was a revolutionary design which consisted of stacking large circular concrete rings on top of each other. From start to finish this contract took only six months to complete. When it was finished, the new Dungeness tower stood at 122ft above sea level with its light visible for nearly 27 nautical miles. The lighthouse was officially opened by the Duke of Gloucester in September 1961, and it became one of the first stations to be fully automated under the Corporation's new modernisation programme.

The Dungeness lifeboat station covers the English Channel from Rye Bay to Folkestone. The early history

**Dungeness
The Present Lighthouse
c1965** D165011

of the lifeboat at Dungeness is slightly obscure, thanks to various records being lost during the early days; however, after the recognised lifeboat service was established in around 1825, keeping proper records became necessary. Originally, a lifeboat station was established at Rye in 1803, with a grant provided by Lloyds. It appears that there was not a lot of interest by the local people in manning the lifeboat, because within 20 years the Rye station was not in service.

Everything changed following the formation of the Royal National Institution for the Preservation of Lives from Shipwreck (RNIPLS) in 1824. This new body provided a Plenty-type lifeboat at Dungeness in 1825, which was stationed near the Martello Tower on the west side of Globsden Gut; it was manned by the Coast Blockade (the coastguard). In 1835, the station was renamed Dymchurch and given a new boat. By the time the Parliamentary Northumberland Report of 1851 was published, the lifeboat used by the coastguard was a virtual wreck.

During these early years there was a great deal of concern as to how the coastguard was actually responding to the various ships in distress. For this reason the RNIPLS had re-established the Rye station in 1832, and had supplied it with a Palmer-type lifeboat. When the Royal National Lifeboat Institution was formed in 1854, it placed a boat at the No 1 Battery site near the point of Dungeness and brought the Rye station under the same control. Within a few months, the RNLI had brilliantly organised the area with a lifeboat on each side of the Rother estuary, one at Winchelsea Beach and the other at Camber. The

Martello tower was demolished in 1841 as part of a land reclamation scheme.

In 1832, during the first year that the Rye station was brought back into service, the Palmer-type lifeboat rescued 11 crew from the brigantine 'Osiris'. Its Coxswain, Lieutenant F J F Henslow, RN, CG, was awarded the silver medal for his bravery. Similarly, on 1 October 1835 the new Dymchurch lifeboat was involved with the rescue of 6 crew from the wrecked brigantine 'Industry'. This incident saw the Littlestone coastguard galley taking the men on board in case the lifeboat was swamped by the heavy seas. Lieutenant John Somerville RN, CG, was awarded the Gold medal for his heroic actions. This rescue occurred within 2 months of Dymchurch being established. The original Rye station was closed in 1901, and from 1910 the Winchelsea station has been the base for the Rye harbour lifeboat.

The Dungeness station holds one very special record: it was the last station where women helped to launch the lifeboat. These two women were Miss Madge Tart and her sister-in-law, Mrs Ellen Tart. Both men and women from this family helped to man and launch the Dungeness lifeboat for more than a century. In 1953, these amazing ladies were awarded the RNLI Gold Badge. In 1979, Doris, the daughter of Mrs Ellen Tart, and her long-time friend Joan Bates, were also awarded Gold Badges in recognition of 44 and 37 years' service respectively as shore helpers.

In the church, which is quite near the lifeboat house, there is a cross made from a broken skid from

Dungeness, The Lighthouse The Fog Horn Speakers c1965 D165011A

the station. The 'Charles Cooper Henderson' was one of the 19 RNLI lifeboats which took part in the evacuation of the British Forces from Dunkirk in 1940. She was manned by the navy, but there are no records as to what she did during this period; whatever it was, the 'Charles Cooper Henderson' returned to England with a great deal of war damage.

On 15 November 1928, the Rye Harbour station was struck by the worst disaster in its history. The lifeboat was launched into a south-westerly gale, with tremendous rain and heavy seas, to help the crew on board the merchant vessel 'Alice'. Soon after the launch, news was received that the crew of the 'Alice' had been rescued by another ship, so the recall signal was fired three times. According to the reports, the crew of the lifeboat did not appear to have seen the signals. A short while later, as the lifeboat was coming into harbour, she was hit by the tremendous waves and capsized; the 17 crew on board the 'Mary Stanford' lifeboat were drowned. This had a major impact on the local community: the loss of these men meant that practically the whole male fishing population of the village had perished.

After the loss of the 'Mary Stanford' in 1928, the station was closed until 1966, when a D-class inflatable was stationed there. A new boathouse was built during 1984-85 to house a C-class lifeboat. The present boathouse was built in 1995, and the 'B 727 lifeboat took up station on 17 July 1996. A total of 3 Gold and 6 Silver medals have been awarded to crews of Rye Harbour Station. Tragically, 18 crew from this station have lost their lives.

Beachy Head

Although there have been several references to a light that was exhibited from Beachy Head in around 1670, the records state that this was not for maritime purposes but as a fire beacon which would warn of any threatened invasion. The first official record of a petition for a navigation light appears in the Parliamentary Papers of the Lords of the Privy Council for Trade, written during the reign of William III and Queen Mary in 1691. The proposer of a light near Beachy Head was a Thomas Offley. However, even though the Privy Council requested that the Corporation of Trinity House of Deptford Strand should investigate the need for a light, nothing was formally activated until the latter part of the 18th century.

During the early part of the 18th century, a local parson named Jonathan Darby from the parish of East Dean unofficially displayed a candle-burning lantern hung in a hollow carved out of the chalk headland. This cave became known as Darby's Hole. It is recorded in the Sussex archives that Parson Darby carved out a deep shaft through the headland, which ended at a gallery-shaped hollow about 20ft above the highest spring tides. According to the records of the Eastbourne Natural History Society, Darby's Hole was in fact part of a cave system which had formerly been used by the local smugglers. Parson Darby died in 1729 at the age of 59, and was buried in the East Dean churchyard. His headstone salutes this exceptional parson by calling him 'the sailor's friend'.

Beachy Head, The Lighthouse 1912 64982

During the latter part of August 1825, Trinity House formally responded to the ever-growing numbers of petitions for a light along the East Sussex coastline. James Walker and his partner John Burges were commissioned to prepare the designs, specifications and estimates for the Beachy Head light. In April 1826, James Walker reported to Trinity House that the ideal location for a light would be at Belle Tout. Although Belle Tout was about two miles from the peak of this promontory, it would still provide a good location for a light which was visible from both the east and the west.

Compared to other lighthouses constructed around the same period, Belle Tout was a squat circular structure, with the keepers' quarters at the rear. The tower was just 47ft in diameter, with a 13ft-high cast iron lantern. Its conical roof was formed out of cast iron rafters covered with sheets of copper. In turn, this was topped by a tall copper chimney, along with a wind vane and a lightning conductor spike. The Belle Tout light was first lit on 11 October 1828. Its beam of light was recorded at a focal plane of 285ft above the high water spring tide level, and was visible by shipping on

Beachy Head, The Lighthouse 1910 62961

a clear night for a distance of 22 nautical miles. After tremendous storms and gales swept across the South Downs near the end of 1898, wide cracks had formed along the walkway to the station. By February 1899,

Trinity House had declared that the lighthouse was unsafe; they subsequently abandoned it. Sir Thomas Matthews was instructed to establish a new tower at Beachy Head approximately 700ft from the base of the chalk cliff. The biggest difficulties associated with constructing a rock-based tower arise when its foundations are below sea level for most of the time. To overcome this problem, the base of the lighthouse was built inside a coffer dam.

Since the Sussex coastline is predominantly chalk, granite was not available within easy reach of the intended site. It was therefore necessary to obtain the stone from the De Lank quarries near Bodmin in Cornwall. Each of the granite blocks was carefully prepared, and then numbered as each course of masonry was completed at the quarry. The stones were then loaded onto railway wagons and transported to Eastbourne station. One by one they were unloaded onto heavy-duty trailers, which were towed by steam traction engines. As many as twenty of these majestic machines would make their slow trek in convoy to Beachy Head, and most of the Eastbourne population crowded the pavements to watch them go by.

During the early part of March 1900, Beachy Head was on the receiving end of an extremely ferocious storm. At times the wind and rain pounded the headland at near hurricane-force conditions. Several of the site huts had their roofs ripped off, and one of these wooden buildings lost its gable end panel, which the wind whisked away like a piece of paper. After all the men working near the beach had been recalled to the cliff top, the engineer decided to employ them in moving the large granite blocks into easy reach for the cable-way. Just as the mobile crane was carrying one of these heavy stones, the wind increased in velocity. The forward speed of the crane increased as the wind blew it along the railway. Its driver thought the unit was going over the edge of the cliff. In an attempt to stop the crane, he rammed the gearing into reverse.

This stripped off all the cogs in the gear box, to the accompaniment of a tremendous noise, but it did have the desired effect of stopping the crane. The sudden halt however, made the granite block swing sideways, which toppled the crane over. Luckily, the driver had already jumped clear when the gearbox started falling apart. His courageous action was highly praised by the engineer.

At 5.00pm on 2 October 1902, the Beachy Head light was lit for the first time. Its assigned light characteristic was set at 2 flashes every 20 seconds. The focal plane of the light was recorded at 120ft above the high water spring tide level. Its visible distance for shipping on a clear night was about 16 nautical miles.

Throughout the Second World War, the Beachy Head lighthouse was used as an observation post by the Admiralty. On one occasion, a keeper spotted a horned mine drifting towards the lighthouse. A message was sent to the coastguards, and their duty officer gave the keepers the following directive: 'If the mine is over two hundred yards away, attempt to destroy it with rifle fire'. One of the keepers told the officer: 'But we don't have any rifles'. After a few seconds' silence, the coastguard officer replied: 'Well, stand by and the best of luck'. For a very tense period, the keepers watched the mine moving slowly towards them. But as luck would have it, the sea took the mine away from the lighthouse and washed it ashore about 50 yards to the east, where it exploded spectacularly as it hit the beach.

When the Beachy Head lighthouse first came into service, her colours were black stripes with the natural light granite providing near white bands. In 1951, Trinity House gave the tower its first coat of red and white livery.

In 1981, Trinity House began automating the Beachy Head lighthouse. During this contract, the engineers also fitted several bright orange plastic balls onto the power cable that stretches from the cliff top.

The purpose of these markers is to warn hang-gliders about the electricity cable, which to date has caused three enthusiasts to crash on to the beach.

On the Saturday before Christmas 1981, the Friends of the Royal Sovereign and Beachy Head lighthouses, accompanied by the Mayor of Eastbourne, delivered the traditional hamper to the keepers for the last time. Beachy Head lighthouse was formally switched to automatic operation in June 1982, just 80 years after it was first lit. On this day the last of the traditional keepers left the lighthouse.

It is a sad fact of life that loneliness, heartbreak and deep depression can force many people to contemplate taking their own lives. Regrettably, Beachy Head has become one of the most notorious suicide locations in England. At the nearby Beachy Head Hotel, successive landlords have stated that they seem to develop a sixth sense in spotting potential victims. Many of these people tend to be alone, and to gaze vacantly out of the windows towards the sea. The kind understanding given to these people by various members of staff have prevented many from taking such drastic action. But not all of the suicides called at the Hotel, with the result that the keepers in the lighthouse were often involved with the coastguard rescue teams following these tragic events.

Beachy Head, The Lighthouse, the Landing 1910
62961A

Hurst Point

Following the Act of Supremacy in 1536, Henry VIII ordered the dissolution of the Papal monasteries. Thousands of monks and Catholic priests were put to the sword or expelled from England. Within 2 years, certain English diplomats had stirred up a serious rivalry between Charles V and Francis I of France, which brought the imminent danger of a French invasion of England. By 1541, Henry VIII had ordered his Privy Council to construct fortifications from Hull to Milford Haven. The money for this project came from the plundered Catholic monasteries. During the summer of the same year,

Hurst Point, The Lighthouse c1955 M303145
The building to the right is the acetylene generating house.

the building of Hurst Castle was begun and by 1544, it had been brought into service.

At times, Hurst Castle was used for burning lime, but apart from a short period during the reign of Elizabeth I, there was no official navigational fire or light to cover this western approach to the Solent. Any attempt to erect a light was strongly objected to on the grounds that it would guide the monarch's enemies at a time of war. The earliest recorded light on Hurst Point was a small wood-burning beacon similar to a metal basket fixed on a long pole, which was erected around 1733. Near the end of the 18th century, the volume of shipping using the western approach towards Calshot Spit and Southampton demanded the need for a suitable navigational light. In 1776, numerous English shipowners and merchants petitioned the Corporation of Trinity House for a light at Needles Point on the Isle of Wight.

The wording of the petition clearly showed the reason for the application when it stated that 'many ships and vessels have been lost near the Isle of Wight and lives, ships and goods of His Majesty's subjects as well as the King's Royal Navy, continue to be exposed to the like calamities more especially in the night season, and in hard southerly gales'. Nothing further was done by the Corporation of Trinity House until 1780, mainly owing to the numbers of objectors, who still felt that a light would be a burden to shipping and an invitation to the King's enemies. By this time, the loss of shipping around the Needles was reaching epidemic proportions.

In March 1780, William Tatnall, a wealthy merchant from Ironmonger Lane in London, acted as the spokesman and prospective chairman for a consortium of shipowners and businessmen. This group of people were interested in leasing the Needles Point and erecting a light. Politics and finance played a major role in the response of Trinity House, which had to consider the need for a light. On receiving the William Tatnall application, Trinity House insisted that it would only consider the proposal if the consortium agreed to build lighthouses at Hurst Point and at St Catherines on the Isle of Wight as well as at the Needles. The Corporation also specified that the consortium would be responsible for providing suitable roads, towers, keepers' cottages and qualified personnel to maintain the lights.

Initially, the first offer made by the Corporation was in the form of a joint lease. Trinity House would pay the William Tatnall consortium £960 per year for a period of 21 years. A clause was added to the Corporation's proposals: if the estimated costs exceeded £2000, this payment would be increased by 10% each year. As for the light levies, these would be

Hurst Point, The Lighthouse c1955 M303145a
The low lighthouse keepers cottage which was built in 1865.

collected by the Corporation, and profits from the venture would go to the Trinity House Charities.

For a short period there seemed to be no firm agreement. Discussions resumed in 1782, when the Corporation amended its offer and agreed to build all the lighthouses and to pay the William Tatnall consortium £760 per year to manage the lights. However, the Secretary for Trinity House made an error in the letter sent to William Tatnall: it stated that 'any damage by fire, storm, tempests and firing of cannons on Hurst Castle' was to be his responsibility to put right. In fact, this was not the case. Even after the Corporation sent another letter in which it clearly stated that the consortium would not be held responsible for such actions, William Tatnall felt extremely offended and withdrew from any further negotiations.

The architect Richard Jupp was then commissioned by Trinity House to design and build the proposed three lighthouses. The Hurst Point lighthouse was established close to the existing fort, and on 29 September 1786 it was lit for the first time. Over subsequent years, it was noted that from certain directions the Hurst light could not be seen by shipping. In 1812 Trinity House established a high light further inland as a means to remedy this problem.

In 1866 the present lighthouse was built to the designs of James Nicholas Douglass to replace the unsafe original structure. This new lighthouse tower stood 75ft from the ground floor to the top of the lantern. Its light was set at 64ft above the highest spring tide level and was visible for about 14 nautical miles. A new cottage was also built close to the tower, which provided accommodation for 3 keepers and their families. However, within a few years the status of this station was changed to that of keepers only.

In 1911, the existing low light was discontinued and a new steel structure was erected close to the walls of Hurst Fort. This steel structure was a fully automatic acetylene-operated lighthouse; today it is still in service, and recognisable by its distinctive red paintwork. During 1995-96 the Hurst Point lights were modernised and brought under a fully automated system. An attendant keeper visits the station on a regular basis, with the main monitoring and control of these lights covered by the Trinity House control centre in Harwich.

TO RECEIVE YOUR FREE MOUNTED PRINT

Mounted Print
Overall size 14 x 11 inches

Cut out this Voucher and return it with your remittance for £1.95 to cover postage and handling, to UK addresses. For overseas addresses please include £4.00 post and handling. Choose any photograph included in this book. Your SEPIA print will be A4 in size, and mounted in a cream mount with burgundy rule line, overall size 14 x 11 inches.

Order additional Mounted Prints at HALF PRICE (only £7.49 each*)

If there are further pictures you would like to order, possibly as gifts for friends and family, purchase them at half price (no additional postage and handling required).

Have your Mounted Prints framed*

For an additional £14.95 per print you can have your chosen Mounted Print framed in an elegant polished wood and gilt moulding, overall size 16 x 13 inches (no additional postage and handling required).

> *** IMPORTANT!**
> These special prices are only available if ordered using the original voucher on this page (no copies permitted) and at the same time as your free Mounted Print, for delivery to the same address

Frith Collectors' Guild

From time to time we publish a magazine of news and stories about Frith photographs and further special offers of Frith products. If you would like 12 months FREE membership, please return this form.

Send completed forms to:
The Francis Frith Collection, Frith's Barn, Teffont, Salisbury, Wiltshire SP3 5QP

Voucher for **FREE** and Reduced Price Frith Prints

Picture no.	Page number	Qty	Mounted @ £7.49	Framed + £14.95	Total Cost
		1	**Free of charge***	£	£
			£7.49	£	£
			£7.49	£	£
			£7.49	£	£
			£7.49	£	£
			£7.49	£	£

Please allow 28 days for delivery	*** Post & handling**	**£1.95**
Book Title	**Total Order Cost**	**£**

Please do not photocopy this voucher. Only the original is valid, so please cut it out and return it to us.

I enclose a cheque / postal order for £ . . . . made payable to 'The Francis Frith Collection' OR please debit my Mastercard / Visa / Switch / Amex card *(credit cards please on all overseas orders)*

Number . . . .

Issue No(Switch only) . . . . .Valid from (Amex/Switch) . . . .

Expires . . . . Signature . . . .

Name Mr/Mrs/Ms . . . .

Address . . . .

. . . .

. . . . Postcode . . . .

Daytime Tel No . . . .   Valid to 31/12/03

The Francis Frith Collectors' Guild

Please enrol me as a member for 12 months free of charge.

Name Mr/Mrs/Ms . . . .

Address . . . .

. . . .

. . . . Postcode . . . .

Would you like to find out more about Francis Frith?

We have recently recruited some entertaining speakers who are happy to visit local groups, clubs and societies to give an illustrated talk documenting Frith's travels and photographs. If you are a member of such a group and are interested in hosting a presentation, we would love to hear from you.

Our speakers bring with them a small selection of our local town and county books, together with sample prints. They are happy to take orders. A small proportion of the order value is donated to the group who have hosted the presentation. The talks are therefore an excellent way of fundraising for small groups and societies.

Can you help us with information about any of the Frith photographs in this book?

We are gradually compiling an historical record for each of the photographs in the Frith archive. It is always fascinating to find out the names of the people shown in the pictures, as well as insights into the shops, buildings and other features depicted.

If you recognize anyone in the photographs in this book, or if you have information not already included in the author's caption, do let us know. We would love to hear from you, and will try to publish it in future books or articles.

Our production team

Frith books are produced by a small dedicated team at offices in the converted Grade II listed 18th-century barn at Teffont near Salisbury, illustrated above. Most have worked with the Frith Collection for many years. All have in common one quality: they have a passion for the Frith Collection. The team is constantly expanding, but currently includes:

Jason Buck, John Buck, Douglas Burns, Heather Crisp, Isobel Hall, Rob Hames, Hazel Heaton, Peter Horne, James Kinnear, Tina Leary, Hannah Marsh, Eliza Sackett, Terence Sackett, Sandra Sanger, Shelley Tolcher, Susanna Walker, Clive Wathen and Jenny Wathen.

Free Print - see overleaf